HOW WOULD YOU LIKE TO HAVE MADE OUT WITH GIRLS LIKE THESE?

Jennifer, an angelic and virginal Chicago sub-deb . . . Gillian, an avid English divorcée who liked to sleep three in a bed . . . Stevie (yes, she was a girl), a bewitching and unfulfilled Los Angeles married woman . . . Irene, the ultimate dream of a sex object . . . Shelley, a beautiful and totally depraved teeny-bopper from Brooklyn . . . Bonnie, a fabulously gorgeous Manhattan model . . .

Dan Greenburg would have liked to, too. And surprisingly often, he actually did—with results that will surprise you just as much as they did hir

SCO

"Very funny and ultimately very moving"
—*The New York Times*

Dan Greenburg

SCORING
A SEXUAL MEMOIR

A DELL BOOK

FOR NORA

Published by
DELL PUBLISHING CO., INC.
1 Dag Hammarskjold Plaza
New York, New York 10017

1

I happen to be a compulsive list maker. I not only keep lists of the people I have to telephone or write or see, I also keep lists going back some twenty years or so of the initials of every girl I have ever gone out with, every girl I have ever kissed good night, every girl I have ever necked with or petted with above-the-waist-outside-the-clothes, every girl I have ever gotten to third base with and every girl I have ever scored with, and accompanying these lists is a series of cryptic notations about the quality of these experiences which are as indecipherable to me today at age thirty-five as are the full names of most of the girls themselves.

The reason I made these lists to begin with was to be able to reassure myself at a glance that I was doing better with women than I actually was. If I was feeling particularly depressed about an inability to get a date with a girl I knew was the one girl for me at the moment, or if I had just bungled an evening by making a remarkably inept and sloppy pass, or if, more likely, I had painstakingly set the stage for a complex scenario of seduction and then

not even made my move due to sheer cowardice—
why, all I had to do was turn to my secret lists of
dating statistics and see that I had managed to
plant my lips successfully on those of an actual female person a total of 458 times or get my cupped
hand onto a cashmere-sweatered breast a total of
113 times or snake my very own fingers under a
skirt and to within four inches of an authentic,
warm, slippery, white-pantied crotch on five separate and distinct occasions, and then I was able to
relax.

The neat tallies of initials in each column did not
of course register the weeks or even months that
might have elapsed between each victory. They did
not register the demeaning defeats and they did not
register the wrenching tragicomic experiences
which could not properly be classified as either vic-
tories or defeats. They only registered statistics of
success for various levels of achievement in the
game of scoring.

The game, at least during my high school and
college years, was fairly rigidly laid out. You asked
a girl out about five or six days in advance for a
Friday or Saturday night date, you took her to a
movie or a dance and then for a snack of something
afterward. On the third date you attempted to kiss
her good night and, if she went along with that, on
succeeding dates you necked with her in some semi-
private place like a car, prior to dropping her off
at home. You began with french kissing, you pro-
ceeded to general outside-the-clothes body-fon-
dling, and if you could manage to distract the girl's

6

attention long enough while trying to get her hot, you tried for bare tit.

It was generally acknowledged that once you got bare tit (second base or "bare second") you could try for third—outside the clothes at first, and then inside—and from there on into home plate it was largely a matter of how skillfully you could manage the mechanics of clothing removal and actual entry, while coping with a gigantic steering wheel and passing motorists and pedestrians, and without calling attention to the fact that you were actually aware of what you were about to get away with. As long as you could allow the girl to pretend that she was merely being swept along on a tide of passion rather than making a conscious decision to permit intercourse, the responsibility for what was happening was not felt to be on her shoulders. Once you permitted it to shift to her shoulders—and this generally happened long before you got to third base—there was only one thing you could do: convince her verbally of the logic and the naturalness and the healthiness and the goodness and the rightness and even the *beauty* of letting you shove yourself between her legs.

I would like to say here that I became a master in my time at this type of verbal intercourse. I was so proficient in the technique that I started using it long before it was necessary or even advisable in the process of seduction, and I continued using it long past the point of diminishing returns—frequently losing the opportunity of scoring in the process. I began babbling about respecting her afterward when we'd hardly more than kissed, and I continued chanting the litany of precoital rites well into bed and occasionally into the very act of intercourse itself.

If the bodies of all us overly verbal, ambivalent, guilt-ridden, urban, middle-class young Jews had been wired for sound and plugged into a public address system, the streets of our cities and campuses would have reverberated with thunderous choruses of JUST LET ME SLEEP ALL NIGHT WITH MY ARMS AROUND YOU AND I PROMISE I WON'T TOUCH YOU! and JUST LET ME TOUCH YOU THERE AND I PROMISE I WON'T GO ANY FURTHER UNLESS YOU WANT ME TO! and JUST LET ME PUT THE TIP IN AND I PROMISE I WON'T GO IN ALL THE WAY UNLESS YOU ASK ME TO! and JUST LET ME PUT IT IN ALL THE WAY AND I SWEAR TO YOU I WON'T COME UNLESS YOU BEG ME TO!

Clearly, verbal seduction is about four per cent as effective as non-verbal seduction, but it did have its attraction, especially for guys like me. I have always been more at ease with verbal than with physical approaches to things. And, to be painfully frank about it, attempting seduction with words rather than with gestures insured that things would not progress too rapidly and get out of hand.

The obsession with scoring which dominated my youth was complicated by the perhaps more powerful goal of falling-in-love-and-getting-married, learned even more from movies than from mothers, and if nice Jewish boys like me took the teachings of Hollywood and Tin Pan Alley more seriously than did our Gentile brothers—and I think we did —maybe it was because Hollywood and Tin Pan Alley were dominated by men who were once nice Jewish boys themselves.

My own obsessions with scoring and with getting married were further complicated by great thumping fears that I wasn't going to be able to measure up to the standards for sex and marriage set in songs and movies. It seems obvious by now that the movies and popular ballads we grew up with gave us a dangerously romantic and unrealistic set of expectations about life (hardly an original thought, but nonetheless true for that), and when our experiences fell short of those expectations we blamed our own shameful inadequacies rather than any lack of realism in our expectations. It has always been easier to fake happiness and shut up about the fakery than to tell the truth and expose the myth that caused the disillusion—even at the expense of perpetrating the myth for others. And God knows I've done my share of perpetrating the myth for others.

There may be some social value in what I am about to tell you. Sociologists of the future may find in the curious courting customs of urban Americans in the 1950s and 1960s described herein the key to much of the bizarre behavior of society in general during the 1970s. Because I think there is a fairly direct link between how we dated and how we married and how we coped with it when it all turned out so differently from what we expected.

On the other hand, there may be no social value whatever in what follows, and this whole thing may be nothing more than a sneaky attempt on the part of a latent blabbermouth to brag in print about his sexual exploits.

I am aware that this book is rather stunningly male chauvinistic. Well, what can I tell you? During the years I was dating, we all lusted after, idealized, resented, feared and worshiped girls, surely not as equals but as superior or inferior objects. However, to have labeled us male chauvinists seems to me about as useful as classifying us as bipeds. I mean, that's what we were—so what else is new? I'm not condoning the attitude, I'm merely reporting it. I believe I've managed to become less of a sexist pig today than I used to be during my dating days; I'm still working on it, and I've still got a long way to go.

Anyway, I intend to tell you here about some of the young women I came up to bat against between the ages of twenty and thirty—from the time I first belatedly made it past second base into scoring position, until the time the game was finally called on account of marriage.

I will try to re-create the dialogues I had with these young women as faithfully as I can, avoiding as much as possible the overwhelming temptation to improve my own utterances at the expense of theirs, or to try and make myself appear to be the good guy in each situation if I was not.

I will try to tell it all as honestly and as straightforwardly as I can, without slipping into flattering half-truths about myself or otherwise trying to con you into liking me—though I fear in looking back over what I have so far written that I've already tried to do this.

2

I'd like to point out here that the "I" in these pages is not just some semi-autobiographical first-person-narrator/protagonist I dreamed up, it is really me. Or, I should say, the me of some fifteen or so years ago. The part of my life that this book will span is from the age I first started seriously trying to lose my cherry to the age I finally wearied of the game of seduction—or, as I just said, from ages twenty to thirty. Before age twenty my attempts at scoring were not serious enough to be dealt with here. And at age thirty I got married, settled down, and became, at least in the context of this book, not terribly interesting to read about. Because the instant I signed the marriage contract and said "I do" was the instant I traded the self-image of Bachelor for the self-image of Husband, and in so doing lost forever any interest in or sympathy for the great bachelor obsessions of Meeting Girls and Scoring. (Or, rather, I traded the great bachelor obsessions of Meeting Girls and Scoring for the great husband obsessions of Meeting Women and Fantasizing. But that, as they say, is another story.)

Some physical description is probably in order here: I have sad (sultry? sexy? only sad?) brown eyes, and brown hair which is just beginning to go gray. I weigh just under a hundred and fifty pounds fully clothed (skinny people always weigh themselves fully clothed), and I stand between five feet ten and a half and five feet eight, depending on how much of a slouch I happen to be affecting at the time. I wear glasses, I have a fairly high forehead with a small scar in the middle of it (the result of cracking my head open on a manhole cover at age eight). I have a rather longish chin or underslung jaw, however you might describe it, which would probably not be so underslung had I not, at age nineteen (after spending a full semester in a college wrestling class without sustaining a single scratch), walked into the backswing of someone's serve on my very first day in tennis class, even before attendance was taken, and gotten my upper front teeth shattered and ultimately replaced by a permanent bridge. I have surprisingly hard stomach muscles, the result of a continuing ability to do fourteen consecutive chinups, which, apart from a brief but successful fling at water skiing, happens to be my only physical accomplishment.

There is probably a photograph of me on the dust jacket of this book as I appear now, at the age of thirty-five, but it was doubtless taken at an angle which will show neither the longishness of the chin nor, for that matter, the hardness of the stomach muscles, so I imagine the one balances out the other.

From the pictures my parents have of me in Chicago I see that I was a really fantastic-looking little boy until about the age of seven, when my looks began to fall apart. My hair, which had been a terrific un-Jewish blond color, began to turn into the dumb brown color it is now. My perky little baby teeth were replaced by oddly spaced grownup teeth which were given lousy directions up there in my gums and showed up in the wrong places, already resigned to years of having little silver wires tightened around them. My chin started growing and my eyes became nearsighted enough to require glasses, and before I knew it I had entered an awkward age that was to last about twenty years. I am just beginning to get out of it now, and if things progress at the rate they've been going, look for me to become a fairly peppy-looking guy by the age of sixty-five.

Within the last few years something curious has happened: my kind of looks have more or less come into fashion. Skinny guys now for some reason are thought to have trendier bodies than the beefy jocks I always used to envy. Actors with handsome faces are actually losing jobs in movies and TV commercials to ones with ordinary or even homely faces. And people with 20-20 vision, for reasons best known to them, are suddenly wearing glasses.

The first time I began to suspect that something was in the wind was at a little gathering at the home of a beautiful Jewish Princess I was going out with at the time. I could never figure out exactly why this girl was going out with me, because we were neither sleeping together nor communicating verbally. I had this theory that every time I called her for a date she wasn't exactly sure which one I was and merely accepted on the chance that it might be someone terrific. Anyway, one night she said she was having a group of her friends over and would I come and bring my guitar. I said sure. And when I walked into the room, there were twelve identical-looking beautiful Jewish Princesses and eleven skinny guys with glasses and guitars. (We should have formed a rock group.)

If I had been a really great-looking kid, and if I'd been a really good athlete, I would have been in there every day after school, practicing softball with the other kids without having to be asked, instead of hanging around at the fringes of the playground, getting my marbles and my hats stolen by the other misfits who were bigger than I was. Yes, if I had been a really good-looking kid, I would have been popular with my classmates, I would have been smooth with the girls, I would have started scoring at about age fourteen, I would have been a big fraternity guy in college, and I would have wound up selling Oldsmobiles.

For sure I wouldn't have had the bitterness and the fierce ambition I've needed in order to become a successful free-lance writer. (Although, I don't know. I've been rationalizing this way for several years now and been almost able to convince myself that it sure was lucky, boy, that I wasn't good at sports as a kid because look what a terrific life I have now as a writer. And then, not too long ago,

16

I came across a whole group of successful writers in East Hampton, and they're all these tall, rangy, great-looking guys with terrific builds who spend every minute they aren't at the typewriter or in bed with a girl, flipping footballs and baseballs and basketballs and volleyballs and Frisbees back and forth between them on the beach. So now I don't know any more. I think there goes my whole wonderful rationale.)

It has never been easy for me to meet people or to engage them in small talk. More to the point, I have never been able to imagine why anyone would want to hear what I had to say about anything.

At parties when I was a very small boy my mother would drag me up to a group of children who'd be having a perfectly good time without me and say: "This is my son Danny—why don't you let him play with you?" We would all wait patiently for my mother to leave and then I would slink away and allow them to continue whatever it was they were doing. There was never any question in their minds or in mine about my being able to fit in.

As a young man in college and for a while afterward, the pattern continued about the same, with the hostess of whatever party it happened to be taking over the role abdicated by my mother, pulling me over to a knot of people who were telling each other terrific secret things and laughing, and always the laughter and the telling of terrific secret things would come to an immediate halt as I was introduced to the group and the hostess departed.

Often I would be asked a polite question or two before the conversation resumed around me. Occasionally I remembered an urgent phone call I had to make and I excused myself. Occasionally I stood lamely by, unspeaking, until my silence became an embarrassment and the group rather than I drifted away.

It's not that I feel I have nothing to say to people. It's more that I feel I have to be coaxed into saying it. I have to feel absolutely positive that the people I'm talking to really and truly wish to hear whatever it is I'm about to say.

Why is this? Could it be the consequence of parents who always dropped everything in order to hear what I had to say? Or is it the consequence of parents who dropped nothing? I don't know. Neither of these accurately describes my childhood.

When I travel alone by plane, why is it that I see some men able to swap pleasantries with the stewardesses, trading lewd winks and generally edging into position for panting couplings in darkened hotel rooms, while all I can muster are stiff smiles and monosyllabic replies to standard stewardess queries? Don't those young honies know I desire their nyloned legs and steamy crotches as much as the garrulous salesmen who bombard them with mindless banter and stale double entendres? Don't they know that beneath my façade of bored and boring detachment throbs the libido of a hot-blooded Jewish satyr?

At the time that this book's narrative actually

begins, I had just completed my sophomore year at the University of Illinois at Champaign-Urbana, some three hours or so south of Chicago. I was on an art scholarship, studying for a degree in industrial design. I was an artist and the son of an artist, and the reason I was majoring in industrial design rather than, say, painting, is that my pessimistic, Depression-traumatized parents figured that was the only hope an artist had of making enough to live on. I was living in a large rooming house on campus, and I was going into Chicago to visit my parents and whatever girl I happened to be dating about every three weeks or so.

I think the way to really get to know any character in a book is to peek into his life when he thinks there is no one looking. Let us accept for the moment the notion that I am willing to let you peek into my life in such a manner. I'm not, of course, but what I *am* willing to let you see should satisfy your most voyeuristic appetites, if not downright turn your stomach. Six and a half years of intensive psychoanalysis have made me a master of the seemingly-painful-but-ultimately-calculating confession. Such tricky candor, as Messrs. Mailer, Roth and Podhoretz well know, is not only therapeutic but self-serving: if I tell you an anecdote that makes me seem an insensitive boor, and if I then call your attention to how insensitive and how boorish I am, you may be so disarmed by my frankness and by my self-awareness that you forget for a moment that the admission makes me no less an insensitive boor. But more of that later.

If, as I say, you were able to peek into my life at the time the narrative of this book takes place, you might have seen me engaged in a variety of private and embarrassing activities, such as: (1) studying my face in the bathroom mirror with a second mirror held in back of my head, adjusting the set of my jaw to minimize its thrust, and in general trying to find any angle at all which was flattering to my face, so as to always be able to come at girls from that direction; (2) studying my physique in the mirror, experimenting with various degrees of good and bad posture, trying to strike some sort of balance between the self-conscious artificiality of a shoulders-back, stomach-in, biceps-flexing stance and the atrociousness of a completely relaxed, question-mark-silhouette slouch; (3) studying my penis in various degrees of erection for the same reason, so as to decide (assuming it was going to be possible to control this) how involved, eager, cool or detached I might wish to appear to imminent sex partners; measuring it erect every time I heard a competitive statistic to see how I stood, as it were, against the competition.

If not alone, you might have seen me peering at the thighs and buttocks of girls wearing tight skirts or slacks, trying to make out their panty-lines, the better to visualize them in successive stages of undress; or sneaking covert glances up the dresses of females of *any* age for a glimpse of stocking top or pantied crotch.

If you were able to peek inside my head, you'd have discovered fantasies in which some dumb girl

20

in one of my classes whom I'd never have the nerve to talk to would by degrees fall hopelessly in love with me, and into bed with me. Or else she'd have to be raped and then apologized to and protected and treated very tenderly to win back her confidence and *then* she'd fall hopelessly in love with me, and into bed with me. Unfortunately, I happen to be merciless in the degree of reality I demand in my fantasies, and so the simple steps of stage setting and preliminary plot development and precoital dialogue usually took so long that scoring was almost as difficult for me in fantasy as it was in real life.

3

In a moment I'll get to the awful thing that happened to me in Danville, but first I want to tell you about Jennifer.

When I first met Jennifer, I was about to go into my junior year in college, and although I had still not managed to lose my virginity (more about that in a moment), I felt worldlier than a European because Jennifer when I met her was just fifteen.

I didn't generally have much use for girls of fifteen when I was twenty. The idea of dating a girl five years my junior seemed odder to me at twenty than did the idea of dating a girl *twelve* years my junior when I was nearly thirty—but I'm getting ahead of myself again.

The way I met Jennifer was on a condolence call that my mother and I were paying her mother and her just after Jennifer's father's unexpected death. I had no more enthusiasm about paying condolence calls then than I do now, but we walked into this apartment which was quite heavy with loss and with grief and suddenly there was this marvelous little girl with long red hair and large tragic eyes which had been tragic even before her father's death, and instantly I forgot all about why I had come and could think about nothing but love.

Girls with red hair are either overpowered by it and turn out plain-looking or else they overcome it and are real knockouts. That observation, like a lot of things I believe, may either be mildly perceptive, mind-crackingly trite or wholly untrue, but it seems as good a way as I can think of at the moment to describe Jennifer. Jennifer, of the latter or knockout variety of redheads, had definitely overcome it. She was about five foot one, she was either very slender or else she gave the *impression* of being very slender, which may be closer to the truth, and she had the aforementioned large liquid eyes which would have sent the Keanes out of their minds in haste to paint her and hang her above somebody's convertible sofa.

With typical sober good sense, I decided that I had finally found the girl I was going to marry, and the details of courtship, engagement and so on seemed little more than formalities, because if growing up in this country America had taught me nothing else it had at least taught me to recognize my True Love when I saw her. I don't think I spoke much to Jennifer at that meeting. It didn't really seem necessary, since we were going to be spending the rest of our lives together.

I remember noting that she was terribly poised and terribly smart, and I remember guessing that she was involved in the arts and took lessons in ballet or modern dance and wrote poetry (I was

24

right) and that the sense of tragedy she exuded would pass by the end of the summer (I was wrong). I made lots of eye contact with her and then I left, saying I would be in touch.

My mother was astonished to hear of my matrimonial plans for Jennifer—not because they'd been drawn up on a condolence call but because my mother had actually been hoping to fix me up with Jennifer's older sister Clare, who had just finished high school and was planning to come downstate to the U. of I. in the fall.

As soon as a respectable period of mourning had passed, I called up Jennifer and asked her for a date. She accepted, I picked her up in my father's light green Chevy and we drove to a very dark, very moody little bar on the Near North Side called the Chesshouse. I ordered a brandy Alexander or whatever gimmicky drink I was affecting in those days and Jennifer ordered a scotch and soda, which knocked me out because it seemed such a sophisticated drink for a kid of fifteen. We spoke quite seriously about whatever one spoke quite seriously about in 1956, and we also laughed a lot, and we discovered that we liked each other's sense of humor. She was, at fifteen, my ideal woman: attractive, appreciative, witty and even less sexually experienced than I.

I inquired with some delicacy how she was taking the death of her father and was answered with detachment. More tragedies were shortly to seek her out and she was to react to them with the same detachment. No doubt she was merely repressing emotions she found too painful to deal with. Or perhaps it was something more exotic. There was a type of young woman I used to meet with some frequency during my bohemian days as an art student—the type who strides through holocausts unruffled but who bursts into tears at the sight of a subway station or of an apartment readied for the movers or of a certain type of tree in the winter. Such people, I think, are inside-out people—exposed and vulnerable on the outside, tough and slick on the inside. Many of them in those days, like Jennifer, saw themselves as Mary McCarthy characters. Today I imagine they see themselves as Joan Didion characters. (I happen to know, by the way, that Joan Didion herself drives a hot-orange Sting Ray Corvette, so there you are.)

Jennifer and I saw each other frequently after that night. I was preparing to leave again for school in a few weeks and time was short, so we went out together almost every night. We went to the Chesshouse. We went to a bar on the South Side near the University of Chicago called the Dock, where some kids named Mike Nichols and Elaine May and a few others had formed an improvisational group called The Compass Players. We went on picnics and we went rowing in the park and we went to movies in arty little theaters on the Near North Side and discovered Alec Guinness.

I'd waited till the third date to kiss her good night, of course, since, as previously noted, that's what we studs were doing with Nice Girls in those days. And soon we were more or less "going to-gether."

After these evenings it was generally our prac-tice to go back to Jennifer's place, sit on the living-room couch and neck. It never occurred to me to go further than necking with her because Jennifer was a Nice Girl, and Nice Girls, as I well knew, would be insulted if you ever tried to Take Advantage of them.

My one previous deviation from this code had been disastrous: while necking with my last girl friend, my hand had unaccountably developed a mind of its own and strayed to the vicinity of her chest, there to fondle and stroke and knead and squeeze and do whatever it seemed hands were supposed to be doing in such places, and it took some ten or fifteen minutes before the young lady could bring herself to coldly inquire: "What are you *doing?*" It was not until that instant that I realized what I should have known all along—that she was wearing false pectorals. Never having sampled the genuine article, I hadn't been sure. In our mutual mortification, it is interesting to note that it was I and not she who burst into tears. Af-ter all, all *she'd* been found guilty of was wearing a rather common artifice, while I, on the other hand, had demonstrated an utter inability to dis-tinguish between flesh and foam rubber.

So, as I say, I restricted my activity with Jenni-fer to mere hugging and kissing. Even this, how-ever, was not to be without its dangers, for one night, during what must surely have been our thirtieth or fortieth session of necking, she looked up at me and said, not at all unkindly: "Are you getting anything out of this?"

"What do you mean?" I said warily, instantly on my guard and ready to interpret anything at all as a slight to my masculinity.

"I mean, are you getting anything out of necking like this? Because I'm not."

"I see." I said, carefully rehearsing my next few strategic moves. "Do you mean you're not getting anything out of necking with me *tonight,* or do you mean"—I swallowed hard and went on—"that you don't get anything out of necking with me *ever?*"

She could see that she had blundered into a delicate area, but she was a very candid girl and besides, she trusted me. "I guess, ever," she said.

"I see," I said. "So, in other words, all these times when we've been hugging and kissing and you've been acting like you were enjoying it, you were only . . . pretending?"

She nodded.

My world—my great love, my future marriage—was disintegrating before my very eyes. And, as has always been my inclination in deteriorating situations, I helped deteriorate it further.

"Well," I said, "if you don't get much out of necking with me, then you evidently don't find me very stimulating, in which case there hardly seems to be much point in our continuing to neck or kiss or anything like that, does there?"

She shrugged. "I guess not," she said.

"In which case," I continued, "there really isn't much point in our continuing to date each other, is there?"

She shrugged. "I guess not," she said.

So there it was. One moment I was sitting on a sofa, kissing my future wife, the next I was no longer even going to see her again. I was baffled. I was shattered. I didn't know what to do. So I left her apartment and did what any normal American boy in my situation would have done: I went home and threw up. And the instant I got back downstate to school, I called up Jennifer's older sister Clare and asked her out.

In my characteristic egotistical obtuseness, all I had isolated from the situation with Jennifer was the one element of it which I could construe as an insult, a slight to my ability at necking, thereby missing the entire point of what she may have been trying to tell me: that perhaps she had never enjoyed necking with *anyone,* and that she was possibly worried or even frightened by this seeming aberration (was this inability to be moved by necking the foreshadowing of something even grimmer—the shameful but ubiquitous middle-class blight of frigidity?) and that she was daring to confess her previous fakery and ask my help.

Anyway, as I say, my reply to this had been egomaniacally masochistic, and I gave up dating Jennifer in favor of Clare. Clare, it turned out, was by no means merely an older and more arousable version of Jennifer, but a wholly different proposition entirely. Where Jennifer was Rima the Bird

Girl—poetic, tragic, delicate, finely chiseled—Clare was Edith the Committeewoman—a practical, tough-minded girl who seemed ready to burst into suburban motherhood at the sound of a C.P.A.'s proposal of marriage.

Back to Rima and Edith in a moment, but now for the grim story of what happened to me in Danville.

4

Danville, Illinois, is (or was—I haven't been there in more than fifteen years) a depressing, low-income, one-industry town less than an hour's drive from the U. of I. campus. Its one industry, as far as anyone from the university could tell, was prostitution, which is, I suppose, better than no industry at all.

Since my arrival on campus two years before, I had been extended invitations on the average of twice each week to join some of the hornier residents of my rooming house on an expedition to Danville "to get our rocks off." I always politely begged off. For one thing, I wasn't anxious to lose my cherry in such an unaesthetic manner. For another, since I expected to marry a virgin and did not believe in any double standard, I was more or less Saving Myself for my future wife. But mainly, I was chicken—of disease, of a police raid, of not being able to get it up and being laughed at by the prostitute.

However, after my breakup with Jennifer (the Disillusioned Lover Giving Himself Over to a Life of Sin), I decided to accept the invitation and go to Danville. Accordingly, one night in early spring, I and my similarly virginal roommate Buck and a jolly Navy vet named Willy borrowed a car, divested ourselves of all valuables (lest we be robbed), and all identification (lest we be raided), and all money except the three-dollar going price of a straight lay, and the three of us set out for Danville.

Willy, who was engaged to a Nice Girl on campus, was not coming with us to get laid (he had embarked on a brief period of celibacy in honor of his impending marriage) but was only going along to guide us as a tribal elder into the initiation of manhood.

We got to Danville about ten-thirty in the evening with no precise idea of where it was we were going, and after several frantic phone calls back to campus for an address or at least a street name, and after much cruising down streets lined with darkened, shabby, single-family frame dwellings, we stopped the car and got out.

What did one do now—walk up to any house at random, ring the bell and cheerily inquire if it was a whorehouse?

But then, a stroke of luck: a tiny flickering red light in the front window of the nearest house. With Willy leading the way for moral support, we climbed the sagging wooden steps of the unlit porch and pressed the buzzer.

In a moment a presence materialized on the other side of the screen door and a tired Negro madam's voice said: "Just one girl workin' tonight, boys."

At the precise moment I had made the decision to beg out of the whole operation, Willy yelled: "Go get her, Greenburg!" and shoved me through the now open screen door and into the unlit living room.

The possibility that the first sexual experience of my life was to be not only with a whore but with a Negro whore filled my liberal Jewish brain with an ambivalence that would never have been resolved had I not been immediately pushed into a bedroom adjoining the room I'd entered and then heard the door snapped shut behind me.

In the light of a 10-watt blue bulb on a bedside table I beheld my first woman. She was not Negro but white, with dark hair and a tired expression on her nondescript face and a dark nondescript dress on her short, stocky, nondescript body.

I had no idea what small talk or greeting was appropriate in such a situation, but fortunately the whore got the conversational ball rolling herself.

"Let's see it, honey," she said.

At first I didn't understand, and brought out my crumpled ball of dollar bills, but she shook her head impatiently.

"Let's see *it*," she said. "Your little thing."

True, I hadn't expected to be invited to sit down and engage in idle chitchat about the cold war or the stock market, but this request still struck me as being somewhat abrupt.

I've always been a cooperative sort, however,

even when asked to do embarrassing things like taking off my clothes in front of young nurses or providing female lab technicians in hospitals with stool samples in little round white pasteboard boxes, so I was equally cooperative in this situation. I unzipped my fly and dug out my little thing and handed it to her.

With a dexterity bred of long professional practice, she examined it thoroughly for venereal disease, then dusted it with a little germicidal powder and gave it back to me. That the "little thing" I'd handed her was limp rather than stiff I viewed with considerable relief, so impersonal and nurselike was her attitude. She instructed me to undress and, in keeping with this nursy attitude, stepped into an adjoining bathroom while I did.

I started to take off my clothes and then I found myself wondering how much or how little she expected me to take off. I thought maybe, just as in a doctor's office, you were only supposed to get down to your undershorts.

"Listen," I called to her over the sound of running water in the next room, "what do you want me to take off here—everything, or what?"

"Just your pants and shorts," she called back.

Somehow I couldn't visualize myself dressed like that for my first sexual experience, so I took off my shirt and T-shirt too. When she came back into the room all I had on, for some idiot reason, were my watch and my socks. I don't know what reaction I expected from her, but there wasn't one. She just asked me whether I wanted the straight three-dollar lay or the five-dollar round-the-world. Although I only had three dollars with me, I pretended to weigh the pros and cons of each in my mind, like any conscientious consumer, and finally settled on the three-dollar job. I fished around in my clothes for the money, found it and handed it to her.

She took it with a little darting motion, then grabbed the hem of her dress with both hands and whipped it over her head. She was out of her bra and panties so fast it wasn't till she'd lain down on the bed, with her knees up and her thighs spread, that I realized her whirlwind strip had been at least perfunctorily intended to excite me.

I stood there in my watch and my socks, pondering the naked person on the bed in front of me and I tried to relate to the odd tableau of which I seemed somehow to be a part. Finally, with some impatience, she motioned to me and said: "Hop on."

I hopped gingerly on, not at all sure where to put my knees, elbows, head, and so on, and not a little embarrassed at having my naked body touching that of a perfect stranger. I was feeling a lot of things by then—curiosity, embarrassment, absurdity, unreality—feeling, in fact, almost everything in the world except aroused.

"What's the matter with your little thing?" said the whore, vainly trying to stuff its flaccidity into herself. "Is he shy of strangers?"

"Yes," I said, "I guess he must be shy."

We both examined my little thing as one might

examine a moderately rare species of mollusk which has retreated into its shell. Finally deciding that direct stimulation was the ticket, she grabbed it and began rolling and patting it briskly between her palms like a tortilla. Neither it nor I found this technique terribly erotic, and the continued rolling and patting and kneading and slapping were beginning to alarm me.

"Listen," I said with barely disguised impatience, "why don't you let *me* have a try at it?"

Reluctantly, she surrendered it to me. And then, in the presence of a total stranger, driven by the growing panic that I was going to leave the whorehouse still a virgin *and* waste three dollars, I commenced to masturbate.

Presently there was a pounding on the door, and the madam yelled: "Hurry up in there!" The whore bounded out of bed and started scrambling into her clothes, just as signs of life began stirring in my hand.

"Wait!" I exclaimed. "I think I've got it!"

"I've got other customers, honey," she said, smoothing out her dress. "I think you better put on your things and go."

"But I can *do* it now," I insisted. "Please—I'm ready to come."

She darted into the bathroom and re-emerged with a wad of toilet paper. "Use this," she said. Unhappily, I had no choice.

"Get dressed now, honey," she said. "And hurry, because the old lady's getting mad."

I was really depressed, as much about the three

dollars as about my humiliation. "Listen," I said, "can I come back later tonight if I'm more in the mood?"

"Don't worry," she said, "you won't be."

There was more pounding on the door. I slowly walked across the room, still loath to leave.

"Listen," I said, "what am I going to tell my friends?"

"Why tell them anything?" she sensibly replied.

But I did. I told them the whole grisly story. Buck was so depressed he decided to hang onto his virginity awhile longer. But Willy, unaccountably aroused by any talk of sex at all, excused himself and hustled into the whorehouse for a quickie.

When we returned to campus, our story was that Buck and I got laid and that Willy remained in the car. But once inside the rooming house I raced Willy to the showers, and afterward we shared two antibiotics I had left over from a recent bout of flu.

5

My experience in Danville was hardly a unique one, but no less traumatic for its banality. In a way, it wasn't even very much of a surprise to me. I'd always known, somehow, that my first attempt at intercourse would result in impotence, and so of course this certainty became a self-fulfilling prophecy. Never mind that the circumstances had hardly been conducive to arousal—the embarrassment of the situation, the clinical nature of it, the unattractiveness of the whore herself, the fear of disease and of being caught—never mind even that I'd heard of several similar experiences of impotence with whores from friends of mine. I was positive I'd be impotent for life.

It seemed somehow logical. I'd always been a lousy athlete—hadn't the non-existent position of short right center fielder been created for me by reluctant teammates forced to use me in school and summer camp softball games? And I hadn't ever gotten the hang of swimming either. Or of ballroom dancing, for that matter. So it was entirely logical to me that I would never be able to fuck:

all physical activities were related, and either you could do them or you couldn't.

Within a few weeks I had accepted my non-fucking fate with a certain stoic calm. Just like Jake Barnes in *The Sun Also Rises,* I thought. I would continue dating girls, of course, to sort of keep up appearances, but I would no longer try to score with them. In a sense, a great weight had been lifted from my shoulders—the continuing compulsion to try and score, whatever the situation. I could relax now, snug in my disability, and contemplate loftier goals in life. I would become a master cunnilinguist. Or a really crackerjack fingerfucker. In time, if I found an understanding older woman who desired the security of wedlock and who didn't find my infirmity disgusting, perhaps I'd marry after all. And, like Jake Barnes, I'd permit my wife periodic satisfaction by normal men.

I never gave much thought to the possibility of becoming a homosexual—I'd barely even gotten the hang of *heterosexual* courtship, and I couldn't face the prospect of starting from scratch in an even more difficult field. (I could just imagine myself trying to make small talk with fags: "Hey, how about that guy over there—some piece, eh? Really hung, huh?" No, it was clearly out of the question.)

It didn't take me long to figure out that, if I were truly giving up sex, there was no longer any earthly reason not to resume seeing Jennifer.

And so, once more, we started dating.

The latest tragedy in Jennifer's life was that there had been a fire in the apartment next to hers —a horrible fire which started when the neighbor's live-in maid fell asleep with a cigarette in her hand. The maid's body was discovered in bed, burned to a crisp, Jennifer informed me—which is exactly the sort of information I can always do without but am never spared. Jennifer and her mother had to be rescued by firemen—the melodrama of which appealed to Jennifer enormously—but their own apartment was hardly more than lightly singed. A few holes had been chopped through the plaster walls and ceiling by the firemen, but that was the extent of the damage. Except for the smell, of course. For several months after the fire there lingered in Jennifer's apartment the smell of burned bedding and charred upholstery and, it seemed to me, of broiled human flesh. The smell appalled me at first, but then, when I realized that Jennifer and her mother were actually living with it without too much comment, I finally accepted it and, for brief periods of time, almost succeeded in forgetting it was there.

Jennifer and I resumed seeing each other as often as I came into Chicago, which was about one weekend out of every three or four, and we found lots of non-sexual things to do together. We went to see The Compass Players at least one night of every weekend. We went to the Chesshouse a lot. We went to the Art Institute on Sundays and took pictures of each other mugging with the statues.

We lay on the floor of Jennifer's smoky-smelling living room and listened to the records which seemed to typify dating in the late fifties. The Kingston Trio. The Four Freshmen. Dave Brubeck, with Paul Desmond's saxophone doodling lazy curlicues around the melody lines. Jackie Gleason's *Music for Lovers Only* and *Music to Make You Misty*, with Bobby Hackett's faraway trumpet blurring all the old standards into sleepy sound-alike versions of "Our Love Is Here to Stay."

And in time, though both Jennifer and I privately thought it pointless, we succumbed to the American Way of Dating and again began to neck. Jennifer might not have been getting anything out of it, and I might not have had the slightest intention of escalating necking into intercourse, but there we were, sitting on her mother's living-room couch like any two normal American kids, with our tongues in each other's mouths. And there I ultimately was, with my hand inside the back of Jennifer's sweater, inexpertly fumbling with the hooks on her brassiere.

After I'd been fumbling off and on for some twenty or thirty minutes, trying to disguise my ineptitude with her brassiere catch as a vague disinterest with the task at hand, she pulled slightly away from me and said in this very quiet, serious voice: "Would you like me to take off my clothes?"

There is no polite *negative* answer to that question ("Oh no, thanks, I was just browsing"), just as there is no non-committing *positive* one ("Oh yes, thanks, I'll just sit down on this chair here and watch"). So I said sure, and Jennifer went into the bathroom to disrobe.

It wasn't fair, I thought. All I'd done was try to unfasten her brassiere, and now I was committed to trying to fuck her. Committed, although I'd already resigned myself to a life of celibacy. Committed, though Jennifer herself knew she didn't get anything out of necking, and knew I knew, and knew she probably wasn't going to get anything out of copulation either (assuming I would somehow be able to manage it). Committed, though the pungent odor of fried maid was still fresh in the whole apartment. It just wasn't fair. Being asked if you wanted someone to take off their clothes just because you happened to be fiddling with their brassiere catch was about as reasonable as getting ten pounds of mashed potatoes dumped on your plate just because you'd politely agreed to a tiny second helping.

Jennifer returned to the living room wearing a bathrobe and settled herself seriously on the couch. That was the worst part about it—how *serious* the whole thing had suddenly become. She turned off the lights and slipped off her robe and pulled me down on top of her and started kissing me.

The feel of her warm bare flesh was very pleasant, but there were too many other factors that weren't. I was way in over my head and drowning and the life guard was giving me mouth-to-mouth resuscitation under water. As Jennifer's not-get-

ting-anything-out-of-this tongue found its way inside my mouth I suddenly knew I had had it.
Nausea spread over me like a warm wave. Babbling idiotically about a sudden cramp in my appendix, I disengaged myself from Jennifer and
backed quickly out of the room and into the bathroom, where I had just enough time to close the
door and turn on the water in the bathtub to mask
the noise before puking my guts out in the toilet
bowl.

So here it was, the absolute nadir. Not being
able to get it up in a whorehouse and accepting
without complaint a life of celibacy wasn't enough,
I was now down to heaving up my dinner in
response to precoital kissing from a girl I considered worthy of marrying. How low could a person
sink, how deep into humiliation and self-hate was
it possible to descend?

I flushed the toilet and then made a lot of cough-
ing noises, hoping to fool Jennifer into thinking
that what I'd really had was an attack of whooping cough rather than nausea. I looked in the
medicine cabinet for some kind of room-freshener
spray to kill the odor of vomit, but the best I
could come up with was a bottle of cologne. I
splashed a lot of this around the room and put it
back in the medicine cabinet. I turned off the water in the bathtub and prepared to open the door
when I suddenly remembered my mouth. I was
unable to smell my breath but I knew it was grotesque. I swished some water around in my mouth
and spit it out, but the taste of vomit still re-

mained. Since the bathroom was sort of a guest bathroom off the living room, there wasn't anything in it like toothpaste. I looked vainly through the medicine cabinet for something I could use as a mouthwash, and, finding nothing better, took out the bottle of cologne again and gargled with that. Then I tidied up the bathroom as best I could and opened the door. I spent about five seconds trying to formulate an explanation of what I'd been doing in the bathroom which might be broad enough to encompass cramps in the appendix, an attack of whooping cough, filling the bathtub and ending up reeking of cologne, and I knew it was hopeless. I walked slowly back to the living-room couch and sat down.

Jennifer had gotten back into her robe and turned on the light. She looked really depressed.

"Well," I said, "I seem to have been a trifle ill there."

"I know," she said, "I heard you."

"I think it was probably something I ate," I said. "A piece of rotten meat or something like that."

Jennifer nodded her head. We had eaten perhaps eight hours before, and we'd had not meat but Welsh rabbit.

"I've heard that's the way it hits you," I said. "You eat something like a piece of rotten meat or a rotten Welsh rabbit, you don't feel anything for seven or eight hours, and then—whammo—it hits you so fast you're lucky if you have time to make it to the john."

Jennifer nodded again.

"Well," I said, trying to inject a hopeful note, "it's lucky I had time to make it to the john."

Jennifer didn't say anything for a long time. Then, not looking at me and very quietly, she said: "Do I disgust you?"

"Disgust me? Is that what you asked me—if you *disgust* me?"

"Yes."

"God, no. Of course not. Why would you even ask me such a thing?"

"Because kissing me with my clothes off made you throw up."

I looked wildly around the room, hoping—I don't know what—hoping that something, some chair or table or something, would come to my aid. "That's not what made me throw up," I said without much conviction.

"Then what did?"

"I told you. A piece of rotten meat or rotten Welsh rabbit, something like that."

"We didn't have any meat. And we both had the same Welsh rabbit."

"Well then, probably it was the dessert. The parfait. I've heard about that too—a really crappy parfait giving it to you the same as a piece of rotten meat."

"You can't get food poisoning from a parfait," she said dully.

"Not even a crappy one?" I said, but I knew I'd used up the food thing as an explanation. "All right," I said, "it wasn't anything I ate. It was an emotional reaction, I admit that. But not a reaction to you—a reaction to the situation itself."

"What situation?" she said.

"The situation of a guy of twenty, a guy of almost twenty-one, a guy who's a goddam junior in college—a guy who's been to *whorehouses,* for God's sake—taking advantage of an innocent fifteen-year-old girl, that's what."

I hadn't meant to let the part about whorehouses slip out, but I could tell it had impressed her, in spite of what she was feeling.

"Maybe I'm not as innocent as you think," she said.

"What does *that* mean?" I said.

"It means," she said, "that maybe I'm a little more experienced in . . . things . . . than you think."

"What are you talking about?" I said. "You told me when we first started going out together that you'd hardly even *kissed* more than a couple of guys before you met me. Are you telling me that wasn't true?"

"It *was* true," she said. "Then."

I swallowed dryly. "And now?" I said.

"And now, not."

"You mean to say that you went out with someone between the time we broke up and got back together again, and that you went further with him than you did with me?"

"Well . . . sort of."

"*Sort* of? *What* sort of—sort of that you went out with someone else between the time we broke up and got back together again, or sort of that you went further with him than you went with me?"

"Well, I did go further with him than I did with you, but . . ."

"But *what?*"

"But I wasn't only going out with him when you said."

"You've been going out with this person since we've gotten back together too, then, is that it?"

"Since, and also before."

"I see," I said. I felt another attack of nausea coming on, but I was determined to finish the conversation to see how much I had to puke for.

"And how far did you go with this person . . . all the way?"

"Well, not exactly, no."

"You did not have actual intercourse, actual coital contact, with this person you've been seeing while you've been going steady with me, is that what you're saying?"

"Not exactly, no."

"Well, okay," I said. "That's something, at least. Not much, but something. How far *did* you go with this person—heavy petting below the waist and inside the clothes?"

"Not exactly, no."

"Heavy petting below the waist but *outside* the clothes?"

"Not exactly, no."

"Not even that far?" I said, somewhat relieved.

"No, further. But . . ."

48

"But . . . ?"

"But I don't know the word."

"You don't know *what* word? For what you did with him?"

She nodded. And then, unfortunately, I knew the word she meant. And I almost wished she'd had intercourse with him instead, I really did.

"You mean you let him perform . . . cunnilingus on you?" I said.

She nodded. "Also, we did the other one," she said.

"Fellatio?" I whispered. "You performed fellatio on him?" The vision of my innocent almost-fiancée with some guy's dork in her mouth was almost more than I could bear.

"Yes," she said, "but I didn't get anything out of either one of them."

I went into the bathroom and had dry heaves. I didn't even bother with the bathtub or the cologne this time. I staggered back into the living room and leaned against the wall.

"I didn't really mean to tell you all that, it just kind of all came out," she said. "I'm sorry if it hurt."

"Don't be sorry," I said. "In a kind of a weird way I know that you weren't even doing it to cheat on me, you were doing it as an experiment— to see whether it was just necking you weren't getting anything out of, or whether it was me you weren't getting anything out of. And also, I suppose, to find out just how bad off you really were. To find out if you were frigid, or whatever."

Her silence neither confirmed nor denied what I was saying so I went on. I said that I understood it. I said that I even saw how it was possible, in a really weird way, that her choosing someone other than me to experiment with could even have been done out of respect rather than contempt. The thing is, however, that even though I understood all of that, and even though I knew she was a very disturbed and unhappy girl who needed a lot of patience and a lot of understanding, and even though I'd have given anything to be the one to provide her with it, I happened to have a lot of problems of my own, as I was beginning to discover. And so I guessed that the best thing for us to do was not to see each other again.

She nodded sadly. "I guess you're right," she said.

She walked me to the door and I kissed her good-by with my vomity mouth on her forehead, and then I left. I looked back once and saw that she'd followed me out into the street in her robe to watch me get smaller and smaller in the distance, and then I turned around and didn't look back any more.

And so that was that with Jennifer, the girl I knew from the moment I met her was going to be my wife.

6

Sometime during my junior year of college I read *The Catcher in the Rye*. No book had ever had such a profound effect on me. I immediately began writing very Holdencaulfieldesque short stories, abandoning them on either the second or third page every time I realized I was merely trying to duplicate Salinger.

I soon realized I was expending more effort in trying to write unlike Salinger than I was in trying to write well, so I reversed field and tried writing *exactly* like Salinger. I took the story of the Three Bears and wrote it in the style of *The Catcher in the Rye,* and I was so happy with the result that I tried the same story in the style of Hemingway and that of James Joyce in *Ulysses*. Figuring what could I lose, I titled the combined piece "Three Bears in Search of an Author" and sent it to *Esquire* magazine. Three weeks later I got a telegram from *Esquire* articles editor Ralph Ginzburg saying he was buying my parody for three hundred and fifty dollars.

I have always been able to make wonderful generalizations about most things in life on the basis of but a single experience, and so I decided that when you sold a piece to a magazine it took three weeks and you heard about it by telegram. Like most generalizations about life, particularly those *I* make up, this was about eighteen per cent true: I have since sold a number of pieces to magazines, and sometimes they reply around the three-week mark, and sometimes it is as little as one week and sometimes it's as much as five. And it is never ever by telegram.

Esquire liked the first piece well enough to request a sequel, so I wrote "Hansel and Gretel in Search of an Art Form" in the styles of Nabokov, Kerouac and Samuel Beckett, which they also bought. I thought it was terrific that I could write parodies and sell them to *Esquire,* but it never occurred to me at the time that I could ever earn a living at writing or that I could ever give up a career in design. I did enroll in a writing course or two, not so much to learn about writing as because, frankly, I knew that I could get an A in a writing course without too much difficulty.

One of my accomplishments at the U. of I. was to form a vocal trio to entertain at mixers, parties and other campus activities. I sang, played the guitar, did the vocal arrangements and generally acted as master of ceremonies for the group. It was a good way to get noticed by girls at these activities, and also a good excuse for being too busy to talk to them much. For a shy person that's not such a bad combination.

It was about this time that I started going through the motions of smoking a pipe. I say going through the motions because I always spent far more time at, and was far more interested in, the mystique of lighting up than in actual smoking. I figured that the lighting-up process would also give me something to do while I tried to talk to girls.

The first time I attempted to put this stratagem to use was at one of the many campus mixers I attended while looking for someone to fall in love with. I remember looking up and noticing to my great amazement that a pretty girl at the opposite end of the room was definitely giving me the eye. I grabbed my pipe, my tobacco, my matches, my tamping tool and all my other equipment and, eyes locked onto hers like an aeronautical radar homing device, I began walking slowly across the room to her. When I was almost upon her I began the elaborate procedure of lighting my pipe. Eyes still locked on hers, a faint smile on my face, I filled, tamped, lit, puffed, lit and puffed again. When finally the pipe was lit I removed it, struck a debonair stance and suddenly realized I had failed to prepare for the problem of conversation. I stood there looking at her, the debonair smile dissolving on my face, and I was totally unable to think of a thing to say. Eventually she shrugged and got up and walked away.

I, who had incredible difficulty talking to girls, was fascinated by the foreign students on our campus who had no difficulty whatsoever. I used to stand at parties or at the Student Union and eavesdrop in amazement as foreign students said wholly outrageous impolite sexual things to American girls, and all the girls ever did was giggle. Giggle and maybe go home to bed with them. I figured if I couldn't talk to girls as design student Dan Greenburg, perhaps I could talk to them as, say, agronomy student Menachem Kronsky.

I happen to be a fairly good mimic, and after I'd listened to a number of foreign students doing their act, I decided to try it myself. I got my friends to introduce me to some girl or other under whichever foreign name intrigued me at the moment, and then I smiled suggestively at her and said in a non-specific accent that was about one part Israeli, one part Russian and one part Mexican, approximately as follows: "Hello, how ees de state of your health, I like berry moch to leeck and suck and bite de flesh of your meelk-white breasts and your honeyed thighs." Like that. And, just as they'd done with the *real* foreign students, the girls giggled and blushed and didn't walk away from me. Whenever they asked me a question I either couldn't or didn't wish to answer, I feigned non-comprehension, frowned and said either "How?" or "Please?"

It was very effective, up to a point. For, though the foreign routine gave me courage to talk to girls I wouldn't otherwise have had the guts to talk to (if I got rejected it was, after all, Menachem Kronsky they were rejecting and not Dan Greenburg), and though the foreign routine covered an inability to be verbally smooth, I feared that it could not cover an inability to be physically smooth in love-making. And so the foreign routine never got beyond the talking stage.

Though raised in Chicago, I had long since wearied of winters in the Midwest with their endless ice and snow and influenza, and I promised myself that if I ever had the money I would move to California after college and never have to be cold again.

And so, shortly after graduation from Illinois, I bought myself a little secondhand Chevy coupe, I loaded it up with clothes and design gear, I bid a mutually tearful good-by to my puzzled parents ("What are you going to find in California that you couldn't find in Chicago?"), I spread out my Automobile Club map on the seat beside me with Route 66 marked in green felt-tipped pen, and away I rode into the setting sun. I didn't know exactly what kind of a job I was looking for yet, but I didn't see why it would be any harder to find out in Los Angeles than in Chicago.

For any normal young man of twenty-one to drive alone across the country to settle permanently in a state in which he didn't know a single person would probably have been judged a moderately plucky thing to do. For someone like me, who could barely manage to carry on conversations with people he already knew, who was so utterly lacking in self-confidence that he agonizingly wrote out entire scripts just to telephone girls for dates—

for someone like this, such an adventure promised opportunities for misery and self-torture to rival the most demented schemes of Sacher-Masoch.

The cross-country trip itself was to teach me a great deal about myself, and not much that I was tickled to find out. The daytime temperature on the trip held steady at 105 degrees. The highway was consistently straight, flat, hot and white, with little mirrorlike mirage pools of heat shimmering in the distance.

By the end of the first long day of driving I was completely at ease with the dangers of high-speed highway driving. By the end of the second I was rather bored with them. By the end of the third I began perversely hoping that something—anything, even something terrible—would happen to relieve my boredom. By the end of the fourth day I started helping it along: by driving a hundred miles an hour and seeing how long I could go without using the brake or how long with my eyes on the page of a book or how long with them closed altogether. I drove in my underwear, I drove stark naked, I drove with one foot up on the dashboard. I decided to see how much of a novel I could read while actually driving and finished the whole thing in less than three days. The galloping paranoia of my solitary confinement magnified daily small talk with service station attendants and waitresses and motel clerks into the proportions of either Successful Relationships or Serious Rejections. By the time I finally made my midnight crossing of the Mojave Desert and landed, blinking, in the bright sunlight of Los Angeles, I had gone through an entire lifetime, like the astronaut in 2001, and emerged, reborn, an infant.

Los Angeles—home of fantastic thirty-one-flavored ice creams and perfect hamburgers; home of palm trees on your street and lemon trees in your back yard and green floodlights on the ivy on your front lawn; home of the drive-in restaurant and the drive-in bank and the drive-in, open-air, open-twenty-four-hours-a-day supermarket that stocks honest-to-God liquor along with the Dr. Peppers; home of you're never more than an hour or two away from sunbathing at the ocean or skiing in the mountains or auto racing on the desert; home of every house has a swimming pool and a patio with sliding glass doors; home of everybody's either in the movie business or just about to be.

I rented a drab little furnished apartment with a fold-down bed in a pink stucco hacienda on a lovely palm-lined street in the middle of Hollywood and moved in. As it happened, I'd been so intent upon the goal of getting to California, I'd neglected to formulate any plan of what to do once I got there, and so I ended up doing nothing. Nothing at all. Nothing all day long. I began getting up later and later every morning and finally I was getting up just in time to have dinner and go back to bed again. I ate a lot of canned macaroni. I discovered TV dinners but I couldn't afford TV. I didn't have much purpose in life or much self-respect. My existence was one interminable Sunday afternoon. I was miserably lonely and homesick and sorry I'd come, but I knew my pride would never let me return to Chicago and admit I hadn't been able to make it on my own in California, and so I stayed.

At length I managed to snap myself out of whatever I was in. I realized that in order to survive economically I was going to have to earn some money, and in order to survive emotionally I was going to have to create some kind of well-ordered daily routine for myself, one that included the twin tasks of actually getting out of bed and actually leaving the house. Since I really didn't know what I wanted to do yet, I decided to do what a lot of people do who don't know what they want to do: I decided to go to graduate school.

I enrolled for the fall term at U.C.L.A. and became the first graduate student they'd ever had in industrial design. I found a job as a live-in houseboy with a moderately affluent family in Brentwood, not far from the university. In exchange for room and board and a small weekly allowance I was to help the lady of the house with the chores and the kids. Every evening I set the table, served, ate with the children, cleared, stacked the dishes in the dishwasher and set up again for the parents' dinner. Every night but one I stayed home with the kids.

There was nothing particularly unusual about the family I worked for. They were, at least on paper, not that different from my own parents, being urban, college-educated, middle-class and Jewish. But their way of life was so different from the one I had known in Chicago that I might as well have been an exchange student from Morocco. My parents had always rented apartments; these people owned a lavish house with a swimming pool. My parents neither smoked nor drank; these people chain-smoked and had three martinis before dinner every night. My parents weren't at all athletic; these people practically lived at their tennis club. My parents didn't know anyone who was having an extramarital affair; these people didn't know anyone who wasn't. I had never heard sexual matters discussed so openly before in my life. For example, one night as I was serving them their dinner, the woman turned to me and said: "Tell me, Dan, what would *you* think about a husband who jumped into bed with his wife's best friend just because the wife once had a *tiny* indiscretion with the tennis pro at the club?" There was little doubt in anyone's mind which husband and wife we were chatting about, and I very nearly dropped the roast beef right in their laps. It was all so exotic and sophisticated and sinful, and I wanted desperately to be a part of it.

I almost felt I was. Almost. My relationship with the family I lived with had never been clearly defined, however, and so it was very schizophrenic: I was both hired hand and eldest son, and I managed to miss out on most of the advantages of each —sufficient pay at one end of the scale, and sufficient love at the other. Further complicating an already complicated situation was the lady of the house, who was young, attractive, flirtatious and fond of teasing. During the day when we were home alone she wore the briefest of tennis clothes, the filmiest of dressing gowns. At night I lay in the dark in my hot, horny little room at the back of the house and mentally ripped the little Lacoste alligator off the breast of her tennis shirt with my teeth. I decided in my delirium that she wanted me as wetly as I wanted her. But, mercifully, I didn't really believe it.

At the end of the first semester I met a guy named Burt Berman who had been a year ahead of me in school at Illinois and was now working for a small design office in Los Angeles. I was desperate to leave my place of employment before I raped my employer. And so, though I'd barely known Burt at school, I asked if I could share his apartment with him, and he agreed.

Burt was everything I was not—a good-looking Jew, a big muscular guy, a player of ball, a screwer of girls—a non-complicated, non-analytical, non-neurotic, non-guilt-ridden, completely spontaneous guy. A Hebrew *shegetz*. He became my roommate, my confidante, my instructor in the art of scoring with women, my best friend. And, without deliberately setting out to do so, I betrayed him every chance I got.

The differences in our thinking about women were very basic. I thought in terms of Friday night dates, Saturday night dates, how many dates you had to have with a girl before you tried to kiss her good night. Burt didn't think in terms of dates at all. He thought only of scoring. He'd call a girl up, go over to her house and fuck her. Or, if she was busy, he'd call up someone else and go over and fuck *her*. He didn't think, as I did, in terms of Meaningful Relationships. He thought of getting his dork into as many pussies as he could, with as little aggravation as he could.

He didn't think, as I did, in terms of Rejections. He thought in terms of temporary delays. If a girl was busy the night he wanted to see her, or if she put him off the first time he made a pass at her, he tried again. And again. And again. He didn't know the meaning of No. He didn't sulk. He didn't let his feelings get hurt. He didn't seem to *have* any feelings. And maybe that's the point: the difference between consistent scorers and me was that they never even *knew* when they were getting rejected.

Not long after I moved in with Burt, a lady he'd known a few years before arrived in town and came over to see us. Her name was Gillian, she was blonde, British, leggy, witty, Older Than We Were, and endlessly *goyish*. I was fantastically impressed that Burt even knew her, much less screwed her. I fell instantly in love with her, rationalizing in all loyalty that she was too good for him.

Gillian, a sort of photographer's model *cum* sculptor, was in town for an indefinite period of time, had an embarrassingly short supply of cash, and wondered whether she might be able to stay with us till she sort of got on her feet again. Burt said he supposed so—he would have steady action at home every night and would still be able to knock off nooners during lunch hours. I said it was fine with me—I'd get to know her really well, and then maybe when he was through with her I could have her.

She moved in that night. Burt got indefinite dibs on our only bedroom and I got the living-room couch. After Burt got sleepy and went to bed, I stayed up with Gillian and talked and joked and massaged her mind into intellectual orgasms. Not as good as the kind Burt was giving her, but perhaps a beginning.

The days passed and then the weeks, and Burt and Gillian and I went everywhere together—to the beach, to movies, to restaurants—and wherever we went people looked at us and tried to figure out who was with whom. And then we'd come home and drink and smoke pot and sit around in our underwear, and I kept thinking that something very orgiastic and terrific was going to happen at any moment—I *always* think something very orgiastic and terrific is going to happen at any moment—and it was all very Jules-and-Jim-like and very Oedipal and very sick.

Gillian and Burt eventually started quarreling. Gillian had begun to feel it might be nice to settle down and get married. Burt was beginning to feel a bit moved-in-upon. Both began to feel used and both began to feel trapped. Burt, who was never much of a conversationalist to begin with, stopped speaking altogether. Oddly enough, he did not stop getting laid.

I couldn't figure it out. If they were so sick of each other, how could they make love? If she was as fed up with his immaturity and lack of intellect and subtlety as she told me she was in our little talks when he was either asleep or away at work, then why did she allow him to continue using her body?

One night they had a dreadful fight in their bedroom with the door closed, in the heat of which Burt suddenly threw open the bedroom door and stalked out of the house. I waited till I heard him drive off, then went to the bedroom doorway. On the bed, in the darkness, poor Gillian was sobbing her little heart out. I softly called her name, then slipped into the room.

Her head was buried in the pillows, her body shuddering with sobs. I bent over the bed to comfort her and in a second she was in my arms, hugging me, pulling me down on top of her. I was out of my mind with sympathy and love and wonderful old-fashioned lust. I kissed away her tears, I caressed her and hugged her and babbled incoherently about how terrific she was and how I appreciated her even if he didn't. I don't know if she was particularly thinking about what she was doing or about what we were obviously leading up to, but suddenly it struck me that the sound I had heard a few moments before and failed to register was the sound of Burt's car pulling up to the curb and Burt's footsteps coming up the walk and Burt's key in our front door.

I almost literally exploded back out of the bedroom and into the living room just as Burt burst into the house. I froze into an absolute cake of terror as he came toward me, but he passed me by, tore into the bedroom, grabbed something off his dresser, snarled something at Gillian, turned around and was out the door again before I'd even figured out a panicked alibi.

I stood there, drenched in shame and guilt over what I had almost gotten away with doing to my two best friends, and I was inconsolable. *I* was inconsolable!

By the next day the whole thing, whatever it was, had blown over. If Burt knew what I'd been up to he never mentioned it. I really don't think he did, to tell you the truth. The funny thing is, I don't think he would have cared. Gillian and I never mentioned the incident to each other either, but it was eventually decided that she was to move out and find her own apartment. There were vague inferences that I would succeed Burt as Gillian's lover when she moved, but somehow that never happened. I don't know why. For one thing, I was still a virgin. For another, I guess she really never could have had a thing for me the way she had for Burt. And, in a characteristically simplistic analysis of the situation, I decided the main reason was that I didn't treat her rotten as Burt did.

I don't know, though. Maybe I wasn't so far off at that.

7

There weren't any girls in the industrial design curriculum at U.C.L.A. I did have one writing class there, however, and there were a few girls in that, most of whom were married. One of the married ones—Stevie LeVine by name—was about the smartest and liveliest of the lot, and I thought she had a fairly dry wit. I liked her.

After the course came to an end, Stevie asked some of the people in the class if they wanted to form a sort of writers' group, and I was one of the ones who said sure. We met every couple of weeks, mostly at the homes of the married members of the group, and we read things aloud that we had written, and everybody offered constructive criticism.

I had never considered Stevie as anything other than a vivacious Sherman Oaks housewife of modern Jewish attractiveness, but one night our whole relationship (what there was of it, I mean) changed radically. For no known reason she was coming up to me and whispering things in my ear, touching me on the shoulder, touching me on the hair, squeezing my hand, smiling provocatively at me from across the room, actually *winking* at one point, for God's sake. And when the evening was over she took my hand, gave it a little squeeze and said in this terribly intimate voice that she hoped she'd see me again very soon.

I was very confused. I didn't know what it was all about. I hadn't said anything or done anything that could have caused such a drastic change in attitude, but it certainly seemed as though old Stevie was coming on with me. I told Burt about it and he agreed. I asked him what I ought to do about it. "Take her out and fuck her," he said.

It was absurd. She was married. She was a good fifteen years older than I. Fifteen perky *vivacious* years older than I, but that didn't change the figure. And she was married. Happily married, it seemed to me. Was it possible, was it at all conceivable, that she wanted to have an affair with me? And if so, why? I asked Burt what he thought. "Take her out and fuck her," he said.

I thought it over. I played out possible scenarios in fantasy. I tried to envision her naked. In a bed with sheets and pillowcases. *My* bed—hers would be too risky. And what about the husband? I had met him. I had talked to him. I had been to his house and eaten his coffee and Danish. *He had been nice to me.* Who was I to suddenly cuckold a man whose hospitality I had accepted, whose coffee and Danish I had eaten?

And yet . . . and yet, here I was, almost twenty-two years of age, and still a virgin. A person who was worried about his potency. A person with a nausea problem. Who was I to be turning away help, even from wives of husbands who had supplied me with coffee and Danish? I thought of Deborah Kerr in *Tea and Sympathy:* "When you speak of this, and you *will* speak of this . . ." I replayed the scene in my head, with Stevie LeVine taking the Deborah Kerr part. Telling me how attractive I was. Telling me I was just as good as other men. (Better, perhaps.) Showing me how to do secret sex things known only to married people in Sherman Oaks.

Eventually, I managed to turn myself on. Eventually, I pulled off the amazing trick of convincing myself I was hot for a woman I didn't even consider sexually attractive. I would do it! I would have a clandestine affair with Stevie LeVine! I pondered the first subtle, strategic move wherein I would make known to her my understanding of what she proposed and my acceptance of it. How to do it—by anonymous letter? By sending her a single long-stemmed rose? "Why don't you just take her out and fuck her?" said Burt.

I decided to be straightforward about it. I would call her at her home and say I wanted to have coffee with her and discuss one of my manuscripts with her. Then, over coffee, if I had been wrong about the nature of her behavior with me, we would simply go our separate ways. And if I had been right, we'd go back to my apartment and we would do it.

I dialed her number. It rang several times, then someone answered. It was a man. It was her husband! What to do? If a man answers, I remembered idiotically, hang up. I didn't hang up. I decided to act completely naturally and brazen it out.

"Ah yes," I said, "hello there. Is, ah, is Stevie there, by any chance?"

"Yes," said her husband. "May I tell her who's calling?"

"Tell her? Ah. Certainly. By all means, tell her. Certainly. Yes."

"Well then, who is this?"

"Oh. I'm sorry. How silly of me. Told you to tell her and then didn't even tell you myself, eh? It's Dan. Dan Greenburg. Sorry."

"Oh, hi, Dan. Just a minute, I'll get Stevie."

He put down the phone then, went to get his wife, and I suppose he said to her: "It's Dan Greenburg—he wants to have an affair with you."

Eventually Stevie came to the phone. Now completely composed and suave, I asked her if she'd like to have coffee with me the following afternoon.

"Is there anything wrong?" she said.

"Wrong?" I said. "No, of course not. Why would you think there's anything wrong?"

"You just sound so strange," she said.

I told her I was worried about this story I had written and I wanted to talk it over with her. I think I may even have said—I shudder now at the possibility—that it was a story about a young man who was thinking about having an affair with a married woman.

She said to meet her the following afternoon at Bullocks Westwood on the upper level, in the coffee shop, at two o'clock. I said I'd be there and hung up, smiling in triumph. What the hell—if LeVine couldn't keep his wife in line, it certainly wasn't *my* fault.

The next day at 2:05 P.M. (five minutes late to make her worry—a little uncertainty is good for them), I pulled into the Bullocks parking lot and sauntered into the upper-level coffee shop. It wasn't, strictly speaking, a coffee shop. It was really more of a tea shop, with lots of doilies and lace and little old ladies sprinkled about, and not a man within miles. A brilliant touch on Stevie's part, I thought, to have selected for our first tryst such an unlikely-looking spot.

Stevie herself was not there yet, so my five-minutes-late stratagem had been in vain. Ah well, I'd try it again another time.

A nice little old lady asked me if I wanted to sit down and I agreed. Did I want to see a menu? No, I said, I thought I'd wait until my friend arrived. My *friend*—exactly the right word: proper, discreet, with just a touch of mystery. The little old lady nodded and withdrew.

Hah, little old lady, I thought, if only you could see me in an hour's time, naked in bed with "my friend," thrusting myself into her equally naked body. Into her Bullocks, I thought, and smiled.

At two-thirty the little old lady reappeared and asked once more if I wanted to order. I said I'd look at a menu, but I doubted that I'd be ordering anything until my friend arrived. She said she imagined that my friend had been detained. Detained? Or had she suddenly gotten pangs of conscience and decided not to come? Was that it—a sudden change of heart and no way to call me off? No, she knew where I was. If she'd wanted to reach me she could have simply called the tea shop and left a message.

At two forty-five I suddenly knew: I had been late myself—I'd thought it was by only five minutes, but more likely it was ten. Stevie'd been nervous anyway about what she'd almost agreed to do, and when she saw that I was late she panicked, decided I wasn't coming and left. I'd probably missed her by less than a minute.

I checked my watch with the little old lady. It was more than five minutes fast: I hadn't been late at all. And then I started getting angry. She had deliberately stood me up. She had either deliberately stood me up or she'd had a terrible accident with the car. I hoped, for her sake, it was the latter.

By three o'clock I was totally humiliated. I got up to leave, just as Stevie walked into the room. Alive. With packages. *Packages from Bullocks.* While I had been sitting up here for more than an hour, being stared at, giggled at, she'd been downstairs in this very building—shopping! I didn't know what to do. I was speechless with anger. Stevie came over to where I was standing and put down her packages.

"Hi," she said. "Been waiting long?"

"About an hour," I said between clenched teeth.

"That long?" she said.

She motioned me to sit down. I was furious with her for being so late, but she *had* shown up. Perhaps she'd had temporary misgivings and stalled for time downstairs to think it over, then decided to go through with the affair and come up to tell me she was mine after all. Could I afford to blow my only chance of being guided into the highways and byways of sex by an experienced married person from Sherman Oaks?

I couldn't. I sat down.

We ordered tea. We drank it. She read my manuscript. She said it was fine. I kept waiting for her to make her move, but she never did, and though I kept wanting to say something suave like: "Why don't we finish up our tea at *my* place?" the words just wouldn't come.

We were ultimately given the check. I paid it and stood up to leave.

"Where are you going now?" she said. Her face betrayed nothing.

"No place in particular," I said carefully. "Why, what did you have in mind?"

"Well, I still have a few more things to buy downstairs," she said. "If you like, you can tag along."

I wish I could report to you that I did not tag along, but I'm afraid I did. I watched while she finished up her shopping, waiting in vain for the sudden frenzied lustful invitation. Instead she said thanks for tea and drove back to Sherman Oaks. I was so humiliated that I didn't even realize until Burt came home much later than usual that he'd

71

stayed away so I could have more time in the sack with Stevie.

He unlocked the door, peeked in, saw the coast was clear and then came inside. "She leave already?" he said.

"We never made it back here," I said.

"You do it in the car or what?"

"That's right," I said, "we did it in the car. In the back seat of her station wagon. Right in the middle of Bullocks' parking lot."

He whistled appreciatively. "That's wild," he said.

8

In the third and final semester of my graduate studies I met a sweet and gentle girl named Ellen who was about a year or two younger than I. She was as virginal as I was, but she indicated that she would be willing to entertain the notion of surrendering herself totally to the man she was going to marry. I was not sure I was the man she was going to marry, but I didn't feel it necessary to share with her this hunch of mine.

We went out for most of the semester and were soon petting both above and below the waist, outside the clothes and in. It was the healthiest sexual relationship I'd had so far, and when she finally indicated she was ready to Go All the Way with me I was so happy I almost believed I was in love with her.

Since she still had curfew at the dorm and since the semester was nearly over anyway we decided to wait. At the semester break toward the end of January we would take a long leisurely drive up to Santa Barbara, which we heard was very green and beautiful, and there for a week in the splendor of sea and greenery we would initiate each other into the wonders of the flesh.

The day we left was overcast and foggy and it was very hard to see the ocean, even though we were driving right alongside it, but the forecast was for sun and lovely weather so we weren't worried. We arrived in Santa Barbara around dinnertime. After some uncertainty about which motel to choose for the big event, we pulled into one not far from the beach and I got out and went into the office to register. Ellen had purchased a fake wedding ring at the dime store, but I felt motel owners could spot fake rings a mile off and thought Ellen should wait in the car. Not that I had to convince her.

"Will this be for just the one night?" said the man at the desk.

"Oh no," I said, suddenly fearful that he suspected something. "We'll be here two, three, maybe even four or more days. The missus and I are takin' it real slow and enjoyin' ourselves."

My voice naturally falls into down-home rhythms whenever I'm out of the big city and nervous about other people's xenophobia. And in some idiot way I figured the fact that we were staying more than one night would prove that we were on the up-and-up. I'm sure that the guy behind the desk never questioned whether we were on the up-and-up and couldn't have cared less if we were or not, but I have never been able to leave well enough alone.

"Yes, sir," I said, leaning back in an imaginary rocking chair and trying to squeeze that last little bit of urban Jewishness out of my voice, "the missus and I have been tourin' all over the whole entire country, and it's a mighty purty country, you better believe it."

The clerk nodded and took my filled-out registration form on which I had carefully written "M/M D. Greenburg" to show how familiar I was with registering in motels.

"It's our first time this far west," I said.

The clerk looked up. "It is?" he said.

"Yes, sir," I said. "But now that we're here, me and the little woman can hardly bring ourselves to go back east."

"If this is your first time this far west," said the clerk, "then how come you got California plates?"

I looked at the registration form I'd filled out. My California license number smirked back at me.

"Oh, that," I said. "That's because the car isn't really mine."

His eyebrows went up almost imperceptibly. I knew that the instant I walked out of the office he'd be on the phone to the state police.

"What I mean is," I said, beginning to lose my down-home accent and to perspire rather freely, "the car *belongs* to me— I *own* it and everything— but only legally. I mean my brother Ben who's a student at the university there, at U.C.L.A. there, it's actually *his* car, you see, but it's registered in my name because he's not old enough to have it registered in his *own* name. Because of the insurance and everything, I mean."

The clerk waited for me to continue. Now I'd not only admitted I was driving a car that didn't belong to me, I'd also created an imaginary brother and instantly made him guilty of being an underage driver and a falsifier of Motor Vehicle registration and insurance data.

"Listen," I said hoarsely, "there isn't any brother. The girl and I are both students from the university and we just got married and we came up to Santa Barbara to spend our honeymoon, and we're both nervous as hell."

The clerk looked at me and waited a moment to see whether I was going to stick with this story. Then, deciding that I was, he smiled. "You know," he said, "I spotted you for newlyweds the minute you drove in here."

"You did?" I said.

"Yep. Don't know what it was—the way you came into the office, the way you filled out the form—don't know what it was, but I knew the minute I set eyes on you that you was newlyweds."

"You don't say," I said.

"Yep. Can't fool a man's been in this business as long as I have."

He congratulated me and wished me a pleasant stay and a pleasant marriage, and he gave me a huge wink and then I went back to the car.

Ellen looked up in alarm as I got back inside. "What took you so long?" she said. "Was there any trouble?"

"A little at first," I said, "but I straightened it all out."

After dinner it didn't clear up outside as forecast, it began to rain. We went back to our motel room and unpacked and started to get ready for bed. Ellen was in the bathroom an unusually long time, and when she finally came out she seemed upset and embarrassed.

I asked her what was wrong. She explained that she'd thought her period would be over for sure by the time we left for our trip but that for some reason it wasn't. And she was too embarrassed to do anything until it was, even pet.

I shrugged. We went to bed and fell asleep with our arms around each other, which wasn't so bad.

The next day we awoke to a hard, mean, steady drizzle. It was too rotten to go anywhere, and there wasn't anywhere to go anyway, so we decided to stay in our room. Ellen's period was still not over, and the only thing left to do was watch television. We saw a lot of game shows.

The next day it was still raining and Ellen was still flowing and by now neither of us was speaking. I'd discovered a nasty reaction to spending more than a single evening with a lady—a kind of suffocating, entrapped, put-upon feeling—and being stranded in a tiny motel room with Midol and Alan Ludden had eased me over the brink. I went outside to walk in the rain.

The next day it continued to rain and to bleed, and I had caught cold or worse from walking in the rain, and so we decided to go back to Los Angeles. The desk clerk gave me another huge wink when we checked out, which I pretended not to see.

The dorms at the university were still closed for the semester break and Ellen had nowhere to go, so it was agreed she'd stay the remaining time with us. Burt didn't mind relinquishing his bedroom at all, and kept on giving me winks and nudges with his elbows until I had to tell him what had actually happened, just to get him to stop. Then I went into the bathroom, discovered I had contracted a severe case of intestinal flu, and I was a joy to live with for the rest of the week.

When I got well enough for Ellen to stop taking care of me, she came down with the same wonderful disease herself, and *I* got to take care of *her*. She got well just in time to go back to the dorm for the start of the new semester. We broke up soon after that, never having consummated our union.

9

I turned in my Master's thesis, passed the oral examination by the professors on my review board, and as a reward for a year and a half of hard work and even harder politics-playing and oneupmanship, I was given my M.A. degree.

My student deferment ran out and the draft board called me downtown for my physical. Years of planning and rationalization were hopefully about to pay off: in high school my parents had virtually forced me to take courses not only in typing but in short-hand so I'd be able to qualify as a clerk-typist in the Army and avoid duty in the trenches. Two semesters of being the only boy in a class of giggling girls was a ghastly experience for someone as timid as I, but surely it was better than being blown apart by a land mine. And then I learned the result of my physical: I was 4-F—my feet were too flat to type for Uncle Sam. It was such an anticlimax that I momentarily forgot I had just been reprieved forever from one of the dumbest experiences in the world, and I was actually depressed. *Depressed*. Depressed that I had just been given two free years of life and a guarantee of never being maimed or killed in combat. At length I regained my senses and went home to celebrate. (Pity about the short-hand, though.)

So here I was, a Master of Arts and free to do anything I wished. What did I wish? The only thing that the experience of obtaining my M.A. in industrial design had taught me was that I no longer wanted to have anything to do with industrial design. I was bored with the engineering end and realized that part of it would become more rather than less important once I actually got into the field. The only thing I'd recently seen that appealed to me as a way of earning a living was the inventive work which was then being done in Los Angeles in the field of advertising by people like Stan Freberg.

Freberg himself refused to see me, but I took my design portfolio around to a number of ad agencies. Everybody I talked to leafed through my odd collection of product designs and *Esquire* parodies and asked me what sort of thing I was looking for, and I always shrugged and said I didn't know. That's about the worst thing you can say to a prospective employer—if you can't tell him precisely what job you're looking for and precisely what qualifies you to do it, he's not going to be able to pigeonhole you, and if he can't pigeonhole you he won't hire you.

As quickly as I learned this important maxim about job hunting, I met the utter refutation of it in a man named MacNish.

MacNish was not a general (his brother was), but he looked and spoke and acted like what I imagine a general ought to look and speak and act like. He was about sixty, well over six feet tall, without an inch of fat on him. He had a gray crew cut about a quarter of an inch long, a deeply lined rugged face and a voice that was only about a half an octave lower than John Wayne's. When he laughed he never so much as cracked a smile, and he laughed only at the perverse. MacNish was the most perverse man I had ever met. For example, he is probably the only man in history ever to be a member of both the Minutemen and CORE simultaneously and to feel ideologically at home with both.

I'd seen some of the ads he'd written and I liked them almost as well as Freberg's. I told MacNish I wanted to work for him. He asked me what the hell I thought I had to offer him. I said an absolute ignorance of the field of advertising. He laughed his smileless laugh and said that I was hired.

Then he asked me what I thought he ought to pay me. I told him. He said that he could only afford to pay me half of that while he was training me, but that he had an idea of how he could provide me with the other half. About a week before, a large dry goods store in the San Fernando Valley had asked MacNish if he'd take them on as an account and do their advertising. He had turned them down because they couldn't pay enough to make it worth his while, but he would now call them back and say that he was sending his new Associate Creative Director, Mr. Greenburg, up to talk with them. If Mr. Greenburg liked them, Mr. Greenburg would handle their advertising himself on a free-lance basis. MacNish thought I ought to charge them the same as what he was going to pay me, thus making up the total of the figure I'd asked him for. (God—why, after all the intimate sexual information I've given you about myself, am I being so coy about mentioning specific salary figures? What I'd asked him for, although it seems amusingly low by today's standards, was five hundred dollars a month.)

Anyway, MacNish picked up the phone and began dialing the number of the dry goods store. Wait a minute, I said, how could I possibly talk to them about doing their advertising when I didn't know a thing *about* advertising?

"Don't worry," said MacNish, "I'll teach you."

"But how will I even be able to talk to them about it when I meet them?" I said.

"Don't talk to them," said MacNish, "let *them* do all the talking—and anything you don't understand, write it down, say you'll have to think it over and let them know next time, and then come back here and I'll tell you whatever you need to know."

I said okay. It was perverse and crazy, but what did I have to lose? MacNish made the call, and I drove out to the Valley and had my conference with the two owners of the dry goods store.

What sort of budget did I recommend they start

82

with? they asked me. I pursed my lips, frowned, wrote down "budget" and said I'd have to think about it and let them know. What media did I think they should go into? they asked me. I pursed my lips, frowned, wrote down "media" and said I'd have to think about it and let them know. If they had asked me what the *weather* was like outside I would have pursed my lips, frowned, written down "weather" and said I'd have to think about it and let them know.

For some reason my cautious attitude seemed to impress them. It was surely not the first time that stunning ignorance has passed for breath-taking circumspection.

I went back to MacNish, he gave me all the answers, and by my next meeting with the dry goods men I was able to tell them everything they wanted to know and I agreed to take them on as clients.

I went to work at the MacNish agency as a combination art director, illustrator, copy writer, account executive, media man and janitor. Even though he was only paying me half salary, Mac-Nish expected me to work long days and frequent nights. He was more interested in my potential as a copy writer than anything else, encouraged me heavily in that area, mercilessly ripped apart everything I wrote and then redid it himself. I'd do it over again and he'd rip it apart again. He yelled a lot while he was ripping and rewriting, and he was a pretty fearsome yeller, so I generally cowered in the corner until it was over. Then I'd look at how he'd rewritten my copy—it was invariably shorter, snappier, more direct, less self-conscious—and I'd try it again.

One day, after MacNish had ripped and rewritten an ad I'd done, I looked at the rewrite and realized with some surprise that it was no improvement. In fact, what *I'd* written was pretty damned good, and what *he'd* done to it was foolish and flat. The more I looked at it the angrier I became. Finally I got so angry I decided I had to say something, even if it cost me my job.

I stormed into MacNish's office, slammed the ad down on his desk and yelled: "I don't give a damn if you rewrite my copy, MacNish, just as long as you *improve* on it! This is no damned improvement, this is a goddamned piece of crap!" Then I stalked out of his office and slammed the door behind me.

I waited fearfully at my desk the whole rest of the day for the news of my being fired, but it never came. The next day one of our clients told me that MacNish had related the incident to him, remarking at the end: "Well, I think old Greenburg is finally beginning to shape up."

Once I realized he wanted me to yell back at him, I was fine. We yelled at each other all morning in the office and then he'd take me out and buy me lunch just so we could continue yelling at each other without interruption in the restaurant. Then we'd go back to the office and we'd yell some more. I learned to disagree with every word he said, even if I agreed with it. It took a lot out of me, but I knew that MacNish was having the time of his life and I figured it was the least I could do for him in exchange for being taught the field of advertising.

Meanwhile, I had been running a newspaper ad campaign for the dry goods store in the Valley which I thought was nothing short of thrilling. I wrote the ads, designed them, illustrated them, specified the typefaces and placed them in the newspapers, all myself. The ads were arresting yet tasteful, informative yet witty, and they practically drove the dry goods store out of business. I discreetly resigned the account and MacNish took me on at full salary.

10

To celebrate my becoming a full-salaried adman
Burt and I and a sort of platonic friend of ours by
the name of Irene decided to give a party. It was
to be in our apartment and Burt's date was a girl
he'd been seeing whose name was Eddie. Pretty
nearly everyone had dates except for me and except
for Irene.

The reason I didn't have a date was that I had
just broken up with Ellen and hadn't yet met anyone I liked well enough to invite to a party with all
my new Los Angeles friends. The reason that Irene
didn't have a date was, I suppose, that Irene just
didn't have that many dates.

Not that she was a dog. Irene was a fairly attractive girl: a rather broad face which was not much
helped by glasses, but a terrific big-boned body,
with an apparently good set of jugs on her and a
pretty nice tush and very adequate legs. She could
have dressed a whole lot more flatteringly and she
could have used some advice on make-up and
hair styling, but all in all Irene was not the least bit
doggy. She had, in fact, gone out for a while with

a great-looking guy we'd fixed her up with, but it didn't last too long because, frankly, Irene was much too bright for him.

And so she and I were more or less together that night, which was fine with me. Burt, as I say, brought old Eddie, who was a lot of fun to be with when she wasn't telling you about her pussy. I guess I knew as much about Eddie's flaccid Fallopian tubes and bifurcated uterus and cyst-infested ovaries as her gynecologist did. I never figured talking about pussy could be boring, but it was when Eddie was telling you about hers. Eddie was a very petite, very pretty woman of about twenty-four who'd been married and divorced about five or six times (presumably for pussy-linked reasons), and she could be quite entertaining in a kind of nutty way whenever you could roll the conversational ball away from her crotch. I don't know why Burt put up with her, because she was functionally out of service much more than she was in, but in a kind of crazy way this very thing might have supplied the challenge to Burt that most women he met didn't seem to offer.

Anyway, there we were on that particular night, Burt and Eddie and Irene and I and about three other couples, and I had been strumming my guitar and we had all been singing folk songs and drinking and smoking pot for maybe four or more hours when I noticed that Irene's eyes had glassed over and she'd sort of slumped part way into herself.

It was a drag to be singing folk songs in those

days and have to be named Irene, because everybody thought he was the first person in the world
to ever make a joke to her about the song "Good
Night, Irene," and Irene had taken a certain
amount of that kind of thing on this particular
evening. I hadn't realized until that moment how
much liquor or pot she'd been putting away, and I
asked her if she was okay. She didn't answer, so I
kind of nudged her shoulder, whereupon she just
toppled over and slid off the couch onto the floor,
just like dead bodies do when you touch them in
the movies.

A couple of us checked her out to make sure she
was all right, and when we had ascertained that all
she was was smashed, Burt and one of the other
guys and I picked her up and carried her into the
bedroom and laid her out on top of the bed. I
placed a cold cloth on her forehead and then we
went back to the party.

I don't know how long the party went on after
that, but it was long enough for me to get pretty
smashed myself and pretty tired, and since the party
seemed to show every sign of going on for a while,
I went into the bedroom, closed the door, stretched
out on the bed alongside old Irene and went to
sleep.

I must have been asleep an hour or more, because when I woke up, already slightly hung over,
the house was quiet. I opened the bedroom door
and saw that Burt had made up the couch in the
living room and gone to sleep, with Eddie lying
beside him, her back turned.

I closed the door and shook Irene gently by the shoulder and told her the party was over, but she didn't wake up. I shook her a little harder and spoke as loudly as I could without waking Burt and Eddie in the living room, but still she didn't stir. I put my mouth practically into her ear and told her there was a daddy-longlegs crawling up her arm, but she was so far below the level of consciousness I could have rolled her right off the bed onto the floor and she wouldn't have known a thing about it.

I shrugged and went into the bathroom to wash my face and brush my teeth, and when I came back into the room there was nothing to do but lie down on the bed and compose myself for sleep.

Now I happen to hate sleeping in my clothes, and I haven't owned a pair of pajamas since I was a little kid. I generally sleep in the raw, but for Irene's sake I stripped down only to my shorts before climbing underneath the covers. I lay there in the dark, unable to move because Irene's body was holding down the covers pretty good on my left side and there wasn't too much room on my right, and I got to thinking that Irene might get chilled out there and wake up with a sore throat on top of her hangover.

It gets pretty cold at night in California, even in Southern California. The houses aren't too well insulated and you have to sleep under a blanket or two, even in summer. I asked Irene if she wouldn't be more comfortable underneath the covers rather than on top of them, and of course she didn't answer, so I got out of bed and rolled her body to the right where the covers were drawn back and pulled the blankets out from under her on the left, then rolled her back to where she'd been, just like they do when they have to make the bed around you in the hospital. Then I yanked off her shoes and put them on the floor and got back in bed beside her and pulled the covers up over both of us.

I lay there for a while, trying to go to sleep, and it occurred to me that Irene might not feel too wonderful in the morning, waking up and finding that she'd been sleeping in her clothes all night, apart from how wrinkled her skirt and blouse were going to be. So I leaned over and asked her whether she wanted me to just sort of slip them off and hang them up in the closet. Again she didn't answer, so again I got up, pulled back the covers, unzipped her skirt and unbuttoned her blouse, rolling her first one way and then the other until I was able to get her out of them. I very carefully hung the blouse on a hanger and draped the skirt neatly over the back of a chair, then got back into bed and under the covers.

I continued lying under the covers next to my friend in her slip, and it suddenly crossed my mind that slips get wrinkled too. I didn't imagine that most girls cared if their slips got wrinkled, but I hadn't ever discussed this particular point with Irene and so I really wasn't sure where she stood on it.

"Listen, Irene," I said, "how do you feel about wrinkled slips? I mean, do they bother you or what?"

Irene didn't reply, and I figured she probably wasn't going to, and I got to wondering. The chances were that she wouldn't care at all if her slip got all wrinkled and crummy, if she were like most people. On the other hand, I figured, why take chances? I got out of bed, pulled back the covers once more, and managed to wrestle Irene's slip off her body. Then I folded it very neatly and put it on the chair and was just about to jump back into bed when it occurred to me I'd never seen my friend so lightly clad before and that, just as I'd suspected, her body was among the best I'd ever seen.

It was true I wasn't seeing her naked. It was true she was still wearing a brassiere and panties and that brassieres could be padded and panties could be elasticized and slimming, and so one really couldn't know for sure.

Instinct told me that probably nobody, no matter how particular, cared about their brassieres getting wrinkled. On the other hand, I knew how constricting those garments had to be, especially for women with jugs as big as Irene's, and I certainly didn't want any friend of mine to feel constricted.

"Irene," I whispered, "can you hear me?"

There was no response.

"Irene, I am concerned about possible strangulation resulting from sleeping in your obviously tight and constricting brassiere. Would you like me to remove it so you can breathe?"

No response.

"Shall I take your silence as a request to proceed?"

Still no response.

"I am taking your silence as a request to proceed."

I rolled her over once again, unhooked the hooks and helped her out of her brassiere, and then I lay her back down again. I was right—her jugs were about the best I'd ever seen. True, I hadn't seen that many jugs in my life, especially in person—mainly Ellen's and Gillian's and of course the ones on the whore in Danville—but Irene's were right in there with the top contenders. They were full and smooth and symmetrically nippled and I felt giddy and voyeuristic and almost incestuous looking at them. I had often speculated on the appearance of Irene's breasts and whether her nipples were round and pink and right in the middle instead of elliptical and slanty or brown and hairy or off to the sides, but I had really never expected to have the opportunity of finding out first hand.

I had also speculated about the rest of her—the shape and firmness of her buttocks, the size and texture and color of her bush—and I realized I might never have another opportunity of finding out about that either, so I pulled her panties off too. I was even more undisappointed with her bush and her buttocks than I had been with her breasts.

I stood over her, looking and admiring and regretting my virginity and not wanting to violate her trust any more than I already had. Trust and politeness and even possible necrophilia aside, however, it did seem like such a waste to do nothing.

"Irene," I whispered, "how would you feel about my making love to you at this point—do you feel it would be taking unfair advantage of you or not?"

Irene said nothing.

"Not?" I said.

Irene continued to say nothing.

"I think it's entirely possible that I may be falling in love with you," I said. "I know you're not too wide awake or anything at the moment and wouldn't therefore be getting much out of it, but I think it's very likely that we're going to be doing a lot of sex things together in days to come, and I wonder how you'd feel about the possibility of my kind of getting started now without you."

Still Irene didn't answer.

"I would hate to do such a thing without first getting from you some sort of token permission, some sort of go-ahead, some sort of . . . Ah, the hell with it," I said, bursting out of my shorts and flopping down on top of her, hungrily licking and sucking and burrowing into her flesh, finally surrendering my virginity to her. And if my technique was a bit unsmooth, who was awake to notice?

I knew it was selfish and I knew it was necrophilic, but still it was incredibly pleasant. I kept whispering to her how much more I valued this kind of friendship than the kind we had previously had and I told her I was *definitely* falling in love with her and just before I came I even asked her to marry me, and then it was over.

I lay there inside of her and my sanity returned and I considered what I had done. What I had done was I had fucked my friend. What I had done was I had lost my cherry and become in a manner of speaking a man. What I had done was I had been an incredible pig. To not only take advantage of the poor girl's condition and use her body without permission, but to have an orgasm without the simple decency of making sure she had one as well. I knew Dr. Eustace Chesser (whose Basic Positions for Intercourse in *Love Without Fear* we'd all memorized years before we'd ever be able to use them) would be pissed off to know that an intercourse had taken place without both partners making it. I considered zipping off a fast I.O.U. to Irene for 1 orgasm, with carbons to Dr. Chesser.

I got up and looked down at poor Irene. (Notice how the last three paragraphs all begin with "I"?) I didn't know what to do. She looked so pathetic and used and gummy. I wondered what I was going to tell her in the morning. "Say, you'll never guess what happened after you went to sleep . . ." No. "Irene, this will probably hand you a laugh . . ." No. It wasn't going to be easy to tell her.

And then a curious thought popped into my head: *Why tell her?* I happened to know she took the pill, so there wasn't going to be any pregnancy, and I hadn't caused her any kind of damage or passed along any kind of venereal disease or anything, so what would telling her about it accomplish except make her feel bad?

I took the washcloth which had been on her forehead and ran some water over it in the bathroom, then returned to the bed. I wiped her face and her chest and stomach and I lovingly parted her thighs and washed her free of semen. Then I toweled her dry.

I went and got her panties, fitted them over her feet and pulled them up over her legs, rolling her slightly to the side and kind of bouncing her on the mattress a little until I could get enough air under her hips to slide them up the rest of the way. I got her bra and put it on her wrong and had to do it all over again, but gradually I got it fitting neatly over each of her boobs. I got her into her slip and then, just to be on the safe side, I got her into her blouse and skirt as well. Then I rolled her back on top of the blankets, patted her hair into place and stood back to examine my handiwork.

It was impossible to tell she hadn't been lying there all night exactly as we'd left her when we first brought her into the bedroom. In the morning I would conversationally ask her to marry me and, not knowing what *that* was all about, she'd laugh it off. But at least I would have made the gesture. Then in a couple of weeks I'd ask her for a date, we'd go out, we'd eventually go to bed, and, in retrospect, the entire event would have been nullified.

I looked at the sleeping girl with a special proprietary feeling, particularly fond of her now that I had violated her. Then I drew a quilt tenderly over her body, kissed her briefly on the forehead, got dressed myself and lay down beside her for the few remaining hours till morning.

11

I have a confession to make to you and I don't
know how you're going to take it, but here goes:
except for the part about MacNish taking me on
at full salary and Eddie talking about her pussy
problems, there wasn't a single true thing in the
whole rest of that last chapter.

How do you feel about that now? Are you glad?
Did that whole imaginary incident with Irene make
you think I was too sick and disgusting to even go
on reading my book? I guess not, because you obviously went on to read *this* chapter. But aren't you
glad that I'm not really sick enough to have done a
thing like that? How do you feel about my being
sick enough to have thought it *up,* though, and
about my representing it to be the way I lost my
virginity? Maybe not much difference, eh?

Maybe you feel betrayed and maybe you're beginning to think that if I told you *one* untrue thing
I could have told you others. I haven't though—
everything else in this book, except for people's
names of course, is absolutely true, and you can
either believe that or not, as you wish.

Maybe you're saying to yourself that you knew from the very beginning that story was a fabrication, that it never could have happened. Well, if that's what you think, you're wrong. It really did happen, although not to me or to this character Irene I made up, but I could give you the name of the guy it happened to if you pressed me for it, and he wouldn't even care, because he does that kind of stuff a lot. Not the cleaning up afterward, I mean—that was my own embellishment—but the screwing of the occasionally unconscious girl. He's not even that disgusting a guy. In fact he's quite handsome and entertaining and you'd probably like him if you met him. Some of your best friends are perverts, and you don't even know which ones, I'll bet. Unless you've actually been to bed with them, I mean.

Anyway, you're probably wondering why I chose to suddenly tell you an elaborate falsehood after telling you so many painful truths. There are two reasons; one is that the way I *really* lost my virginity is a good deal less interesting than what I told you in the previous chapter. (I'll tell you about it in just a minute and you'll see I'm right.) The second reason is that the story in the preceding chapter is actually a part of a novel I wrote a couple of years ago and decided not to publish, and I thought I might be able to salvage it by using it in this book. I wasn't even going to say anything about its not being true, but then two things happened that worried me: one was that I got these incredible conscience pangs about deceiving you,

and the other is that the story I made up had begun to seem more real to me than what actually
happened, and I found that *quite* disturbing.

So that's why I did it. I hope you're not too angry. Now I'll tell you how I *really* lost my virginity.

What happened was that I was fixed up with
this girl on a blind date on, of all nights, New
Year's Eve. I'm not going to tell you her real name
for obvious reasons, and the story is so short it
isn't even worth thinking up a pseudonym for her
and creating a whole character for her, but anyway we hit it off right away, starting with a mutual
acknowledgment about what creeps we both must
be if we had to be fixed up with a blind date on
New Year's Eve.

This girl was as frank about her pussy as Eddie
was about hers (I've met quite a few girls since
then who were obsessed with their pussies—all the
rest were obsessed with their boobs), and she told
me that although she'd had a couple of affairs with
men she was still technically a virgin. I asked her
why, and of course she told me in great detail. It
seemed she had a kind of weird reaction every
time a guy was about to enter her: she got a very
constricting vaginal spasm and became completely
impenetrable.

Well, I told her about *my* being a technical virgin too, and one thing led to another, and the next
thing you know we had gone back to my place and
taken off our clothes, and she was demonstrating
how this vaginal spasm thing of hers worked. And
it did work—it was terrific. Well, anyway, the

whole thing being so clinical and scientific and everything took a lot of the pressure off of me, so I felt just great—not nervous or nauseous or anything. I love the role of healer anyway, since it gives you a chance to concentrate on someone else's problems and gives you the temporary illusion of having none of your own, so I told her to stay over that night and we would cuddle and talk and be very tender with each other, and from time to time we'd check and see whether the old spasm was still working.

She said okay, and now a lot of pressure was off her too, since she'd told me all about this business straight out, before we'd gone through the moves of the seduction game and created a whole lot of expectations centered on her crotch.

Well, to make a long story short, it worked. Not the first time we tried it or even the second or third, but eventually it worked. And you may not believe this because it's so dopey, but we were both so happy and so grateful to see it happening and to be finally overcoming our respective problems and entering the world of relative sexual normalcy that we both came within seconds of each other.

So there it is, the true story. Come to think of it, I guess it's not quite as boring as I thought it was. Come to think of it, it's a lot better story than the one I made up.

12

Losing my virginity made me feel infinitely older, worldlier, prone to smile tolerantly on the romantic involvements of the younger boys and girls I saw —until it occurred to me that they'd probably all been getting laid since they were fourteen.

Losing my virginity was a tremendous relief. Like a man who has always been terrified of water discovering he can float on his back. I waded, if you will forgive the metaphor, right into the sexual waters and had a few quick affairs: one with the young lady to whom I'd surrendered my cherry (who unfortunately continued to be even more pre-occupied with her pussy and its problems than before), one with a secretary at my ad agency, and one with a next-door neighbor.

Losing my virginity caused the image of my ideal woman to change from that of untouched virgin to someone who'd slept around just enough to appreciate how good I now thought I was in bed.

Remembering the teachings of the good Dr. Chesser, I made certain that all my sex partners had an ample share of orgasms, sometimes even at the expense of my own. I mean you really can delay your own climax so long and become so obsessed with that of your partner that you end up cheating yourself. Still, the notion that I might be giving more than I was getting was not a bad way to transfer my own guilt about being involved in such unwholesome activity in the first place: "No, no, go ahead, better *you* enjoy yourself—never mind about me."

There were good times: a long leisurely drive along the coastal highway between Los Angeles and San Francisco, screwing at each Historic Marker; screwing standing up on the roof of a San Francisco hotel; screwing under water at night in somebody's swimming pool; being at a hopelessly stuffy dinner party and slipping off to the bathroom with my date for seven minutes of sexual satisfaction.

There were bad times: meticulously setting up my apartment for the seduction of a young art student, leaving the place with soft lights lit, a fire snapping in the fireplace and an impossibly high stack of LPs on the turntable, then returning to the apartment with the young woman and, while getting out of the car, stepping suavely into dog shit; tenderly undressing an affectionate girl in the darkness and then being warned not to touch her above the waist because she had no breasts, and not being sure whether she was merely telling me in melodramatic fashion that she believed them smallish (I have yet to meet a woman who does not believe her breasts are either too small or too large), or whether they had in fact been surgically removed; going back to the apartment of a tipsy older woman after dinner, being undressed by her on the bed and prepared for fellatio, then watching in stupefied silence as she drew my member into her mouth and then instantaneously coughed it and her entire dinner out over my outraged bare belly.

And throughout both good times and bad, the sad fact was that I felt no nearer to falling in love and getting married—my real goals—than I'd been as a virgin.

Meanwhile, in the ad agency, MacNish went off on a two-week business trip, leaving me in charge of creative matters in the five-man office during his absence. Upon his return he found things running even more smoothly than when he left, so he fired me.

I was dumfounded. Why was I being fired? MacNish had no answer for me, but I later rationalized that a man who had hired me because I knew nothing about advertising might also be a man who would fire me once he felt he had nothing further to teach me.

After twenty-four hours of hustling I landed a job as a copy writer at a much larger agency, at a fifty per cent increase in salary. The new place had handsome modern offices, its very own company screening room, its very own company ice cream freezer, its very own company politics. It also had Muzak.

The Muzak went on relentlessly, even at night

when no one was there. (Philosophical question: If Muzak plays in the forest and there is no one there to hear it . . .) I frequently worked late at the office, trying not to pay attention as the Muzak served up all the songs of my youth—old friends now pickled in mason jars, creaking past on a conveyer belt. Barely recognizable remains of Leroy Anderson's "Blue Tango," Nat King Cole's "Too Young," Patti Page's "Tennessee Waltz," the Four Aces' "Tell Me Why" and "I'm Yours" and "Perfidia," Mario Lanza's "Be My Love" and "Because You're Mine," Tony Bennett's "Because of You" and "Rags to Riches" and "Cold Cold Heart," the Four Freshmen's "Graduation Day," the Four Lads' "Moments to Remember."

I could identify almost every song with a girl I'd dated in either high school or college. I remembered the special significance the words of these songs always had for me at the time, describing either what I felt or what I thought I ought to be feeling. I still knew all the lyrics by heart, which made it difficult to concentrate on what I was writing—not ads for the company but short stories I was trying to sell to magazines. Despite the Muzak, it was still easier to work at the office than at home, because of the superior typewriter and so forth. Also it was not a bad thing to be seen typing madly away whenever any of the executives who were working late themselves happened to pass my office.

Things were not going wonderfully well for me in the area of free-lance writing at that point. After selling my first four pieces to *Esquire* and having two of them anthologized in collections of American and British satire, my luck ran out. I somehow managed to run up a bewildering total of one hundred consecutive rejection slips from various magazines in New York. True, most of these rejections were for short stories, and short stories have *never* been easy to sell. Also, I was simply mailing them out blindly to addresses in *The Writer's Yearbook* rather than writing with a particular market in mind, which further diminished my chances of success.

Things were not going wonderfully well for me in the area of women either. Even in the new and larger agency I had soon used up the supply of available females. There was no one left who was either eligible or untried. The ones in my immediate environment were as thoroughly picked over as popcorn at the bottom of the box. Since I have always been too shy to pick up ladies in bars, I was in fairly sorry shape.

A hot-shot account executive friend of mine from New York, a good-looking blond Jewish guy with show biz connections and an extended wheeze for a laugh, told me about a thing he'd pulled in Manhattan and it intrigued the hell out of me. He and a friend had run an ambiguous ad for models in the classified sections of all New York newspapers. They rented an impressive suite of offices for a week, complete with switchboard and receptionist, and they interviewed all applicants. They sat behind their desks and filled out elaborately coded cards which rated each applicant on face, breasts, buttocks, legs and probable ease of being bedded, and when they were done they had processed more than a thousand girls of all ages and descriptions, and it took them five years to finish screwing just the *better* ones on the list.

The idea appealed to me enormously, as much for its perversity as for its logic: after all, if I were any good as a writer of effective ads, and I humbly felt I was, then it was only logical that I write an ad to get what I wanted most in life—a lover and wife.

Needless to say, I was unable to state in my ad what I was really looking for—no reputable publication would have run it. Even if they had, I wouldn't have wanted to screw the type of girl who might answer such an ad, much less marry her. Because I wanted to be more discriminating than my account executive friend, I wrote my ad not for models but for a girl Friday, and then I sent it in to the Los Angeles *Times*. My ad stipulated that applicants be attractive, be between the ages of twenty-one and twenty-four, be college graduates, and that they reply not by phone but by letter, telling about themselves and stating their qualifications for the job.

I sensed that I had gotten the whole thing slightly wrong and showed my ad to the account executive. He burst out laughing. I explained to him that I was just trying to get a better class of girl, but he laughed all the harder.

The funny thing was that, despite the impossible

restrictions I'd put into my ad, I still got more than fifty replies—not the thousand or more my friend had gotten, but a fair response for the high standards I had insisted upon. I selected the twelve most intriguing letters, phoned the girls who'd written them and made very businesslike appointments with them in my office during the next two days. On the phone they sounded like twelve winners.

The story I'd told them on the phone was that I and two other young guys in the office were thinking of splitting away and forming our own agency. We were secretly pitching five of the existing agency's smaller accounts, and if any three of them decided to come with us we'd be in business. I said that I was interviewing applicants for the position of girl Friday and office manager, and the whole thing had to be kept very hush-hush lest the agency we worked for find out about it.

My plan was to screen all the applicants in person, then call back each of the good ones a week or so later and say that two of the accounts had dropped out of the picture but that the other three looked very good, and that since the girl I was speaking to was one of the finalists for the job I wanted her to meet my partners for a drink after work. I would get Burt or one of my friends at the agency to play the role of my partner, and the meeting over cocktails would put the whole thing on a semi-social basis. A week after that I would call each of the girls in turn and gloomily announce that one of the remaining three accounts had dropped out, that the formation of our own agency now seemed highly unlikely, that I was terribly depressed, and that, seeing as how she was the very girl we had picked for the job, why didn't the two of us go to dinner and console each other.

Not a bad little plan, I felt, and I eagerly awaited the first of my interviews.

On the first day of interviews I processed six girls. Only two of them were even moderately attractive, and of those one had never finished high school, much less college, and the other one was closer to fifty than twenty-four. The second day of interviews wasn't even as good as that, and when I saw that the last interview of the day was a girl in a wheel chair I knew that the entire plan had been a grotesque mistake. I felt wretched and guilty and I didn't make any more appointments. I also knew that no girl in a wheel chair had ever answered the ad of my friend the account executive, or if any had it wouldn't have bothered him at all.

So here I was after all my trouble, with only two even remotely attractive women, and one of them was so dumb I couldn't even talk to her, and the other one was old enough to be, if not my mother, then at least my spinsterly aunt. I decided not to carry any of my interviewees into Phase Two.

Oddly enough, about a week later, just about the time I *would* have swung into Phase Two, the lady who was old enough to be my aunt called *me*. She was quite charming and she had a nice sense of humor, and I had programed myself for Phase Two anyway, so I told her the lie about losing two of the five accounts, whereupon *she* asked *me* if I wanted to meet her after work for a drink and talk it over. I figured what the hell. I said sure.

We had a fairly enjoyable time over drinks, and several times I was tempted to extend drinks into dinner and then into going back to my apartment. But I just couldn't see making a pass at someone that old, at someone who—as good a time as I knew she was having with me—would have had an even better time, I knew, with my mother. Not that the lady wasn't attractive. She was. And beyond the gray hair and the sensible shoes she was probably even a sensual person as well. I definitely decided not to ask her to have dinner with me, but somehow I asked her anyway.

Dinner was just as enjoyable as cocktails, and afterward I offered to drive her home. On the way there I vacillated with every passing block between continuing on to my place and merely taking her to her own apartment. When we reached her street the decision was currently on the negative swing, so I opened the door for her and said good night and that was that.

Things in Los Angeles were getting fairly grim. Not only didn't I have anyone to fall in love with or make love to, but the owners of the ad agency I worked for and I had become rather disenchanted with each other. In fact, let's be honest about it: after little more than a year there, I had been fired. I thought I was doing a pretty good job for them and I demanded to know why I was being fired, but they couldn't seem to come up with a reason.

I couldn't face the prospect of being fired from both my first two jobs so, idiotically, I said that if they couldn't tell me why they were firing me I wouldn't leave. Either they really didn't have a legitimate reason to fire me or else they just didn't care that much one way or another, because they didn't press the point and I simply stayed on and continued to draw my salary.

About the time I would have swung into Phase Three of my now defunct Girl Friday Recruitment Program, the lady with the sensible shoes (Sophie, her depressing mother's-friend's-type name was Sophie) called up to see how plans for the new ad agency were shaping up. I couldn't think of anything else to say, so I told her what I'd programed myself to say in Phase Three: the lie about losing the third account and not being able to form the new company now.

Sophie expressed her sympathy and then she asked me if I wanted to have dinner with her and talk it over. I had the eerie feeling that the entire campaign had been engineered not by me but by Sophie, but I had nothing better to do that night so I agreed.

We had another pleasant dinner at a small French restaurant near my office, and as we chatted and ate and drank I kept drifting into fantasies of sex with Sophie. At times it seemed preposterous. At times it didn't seem so preposterous. After dinner we got into my car and the indecision I'd experienced during the meal now became a raging battle in my brain. As it happened, at the moment

112

we actually turned down her street this time the battle had seesawed to the go-ahead side, and so I asked her if she would like to come back to my apartment.

It seemed a fairly bald invitation and I expected her to be insulted, but she wasn't. I still believed that nice girls were insulted if you made a pass at them and never trusted you after that, and I still believed it was vitally important to have girls trust you or else they'd never go to bed with you. A nice girl who went to bed with you was still *somewhat* of a contradiction to me—and Sophie was nice but by no means a girl; however, that was the way my mind operated in those days.

We got back to my apartment, I built a fire in the fireplace, poured us some drinks, put on some records, and we lay down on the floor in front of the fire. After a time, emboldened by the drinks, I leaned over and kissed her. She didn't seem to mind. I wouldn't say she was a caged tigress, but she didn't seem to mind. She did have a slightly musty aunt-smell about her, but necking with her soon began to turn me on anyway. We lay in front of the fire and necked and rolled around for a while, and then I edged one hand down her body and under her skirt and up her leg and practically all the way up to her crotch before hitting panty girdle. There is nothing to do about a panty girdle, even if you are a professional rapist, except ask the lady to remove it, and so that is what I did.

It was a big mistake. What I said before about needing to let a girl think you weren't aware of what you might be about to get away with is apparently no truer for young cuties than it is for ladies in the sensible-shoe set. Old Sophie was outraged. What could I possibly have in mind? she said. What did it *seem* like? I said. She couldn't understand where I could possibly have gotten the Wrong Idea about her, she said. Possibly from the general necking and fondling that had been going on up to that point, I said. That had to do strictly with friendship, she said, not with lust but with strictly platonic friendship.

I got up and put on my jacket. Where was I going? she said. To take her home, I said. But why? she said. Because I already had all the platonic friends I could handle, I said—what I didn't have were persons to go to bed with. She said she couldn't be of any help in that area. I took her home.

I was confused and embarrassed and hurt. Not only had I been rejected, I had been rejected by a person I never should have made a pass at in the first place but who'd encouraged me to do so, it seemed, and who'd then tried to act the part of the Morally Outraged Woman.

When I got to work the next morning there was a huge bouquet of flowers on my desk. They were from Sophie. The next day there was a large box of candy. I called to thank her and she suggested we have dinner. A strictly platonic dinner? Yes, she said. I told her I was sorry. Besides, I had recently decided that my life was grimmer than I deserved and was taking steps to effect a change. I had just that morning quit my job (assuming that a person who has already been fired six months before can be said to have quit his job), and I was leaving town for a while. I was about to take a four- or five-month solo trip through Europe—an even more masochistic project than moving to Los Angeles had been.

Sophie was sorry to hear I was leaving and wished to buy me something for my trip. What did I need? Nothing, thanks, I said. Nothing? I assured her that I already had everything I could possibly use, except, of course, a piece of ass. How about soap, she said, did I have enough soap? I told her I expected they had soap over there and bade her a tearless farewell.

A week or so later I left for Europe.

I suppose it will not surprise you to learn that at every American Express office in every major city I passed through in Europe there was a parcel of soap waiting for me from good old ambivalent Sophie.

13

Before sailing for Europe on the S. S. *Flandre* I spent several days in New York trying to rustle up some article assignments from a number of magazines I'd been in contact with before leaving Los Angeles. One of the magazines I went up to was *Eros,* a hard-cover quarterly on sex published by Ralph Ginzburg, which is now defunct, owing to one of the more curious obscenity suits of our era.

The reason I went up to *Eros* was that Ginzburg, in his previous job as articles editor at *Esquire*, had been the man responsible for my very first professional sale—a fact which, when I pointed it out to him, caused Ginzburg to repeat several times in a voice full of Brooklyn-accented wonderment, "I dis-*cuh*-vuhed you . . . I dis-*cuh*-vuhed you. . . ." The feat of having discuhvuhed me seems, even today, uniquely unremarkable. That someone was claiming it back in 1962 I found wholly irresistible. Ginzburg can be one hell of a charming guy.

I only had one article idea for *Eros:* a story on the private strip clubs which had just opened in the

Soho district of London. Ginzburg not only gave me the assignment and agreed to let me shoot my own photographs, he gave me an assignment to do in New York before I left, he bought a short story I had written, and he offered me a job as managing editor of *Eros*. As I say, a charming guy.

I thanked him for everything, including the job offer, but told him I had no particular desire to quit either Los Angeles or the advertising business. He begged me to think it over anyway. I said I would. Then I packed my single suitcase with drip-dry shirts, drip-dry socks, drip-dry underwear and a bottle of Woolite, and I boarded the *Flandre*.

Halfway across the Atlantic I got a radiogram. It was from Ginzburg, wishing me a pleasant voyage and again urging me to take the job at *Eros* upon my return. Along with soap from Sophie, I was to find a letter from Ginzburg at every Amercan Express in Europe, repeating his job offer.

I spent an increasingly lonely and paranoid four to five months wandering through England, Scotland, Ireland, France, Switzerland, Israel, and Italy. One night, while walking the deserted streets of some small southern Italian town, I passed a movie theater and saw that an old Audie Murphy war picture was playing. Suddenly desperate to hear English spoken, even by Audie Murphy, I bought a ticket and entered the theater, only to find that of course the entire sound track had been re-recorded in Italian. I sank down in my seat and watched Audie Murphy yell *"Avanti!"* for an hour and a half, the tears rolling down my cheeks.

It was clearly time to go back home. The next day I took a train to the closest major city I could find and booked passage back to America.

14

So physically and emotionally exhausted was I when I came back from Europe that when Ralph Ginzburg once more dangled the managing editorship of *Eros* in front of me—with its attendant promises of power, money and lurid sexual carryings-on—I was too weak to resist. I called Burt in Los Angeles, had him arrange to sell my car and ship the rest of my stuff to New York. Then I went and rented an unfurnished apartment on the East Side of Manhattan and started working for *Eros* immediately.

The power I'd been promised at *Eros* consisted of overseeing a staff of three editors who held me in barely concealed contempt, perhaps less for my ignorance of publishing procedures than for my having been brought in over their heads to take a position that each of them had secretly thought he was in line for. Two of them quit soon after my arrival.

The money I'd been promised, though considerably more than I'd been making in advertising for a standard forty-hour week, averaged down to something close to the legal minimum wage once I found myself working there literally seven days and nights a week.

The lurid sexual carryings-on during those first few weeks at *Eros* were roughly on a par with the high jinks at, say, the *Christian Science Monitor*. I don't truthfully know what I had expected to find at *Eros*—topless editorial conferences or girls in the mailroom clad only in Pitney-Bowes postage strips—but working in the office of a sex magazine turned out to be no different from working in any other kind of office.

If anything, it was worse. There were plenty of erotic photographs and drawings and manuscripts to arouse me, but virtually no opportunities for release. The female members of the staff were either happily married or elderly or both, besides which I had neither the time to see women outside the office nor any way of meeting them. And so I was obliged to process wildly erotic material into print rather than into flesh, and every day my frustration increased.

The *Eros* offices themselves were not unpleasant to work in. The building on West Fortieth Street was old, but it had a sort of shoddy character about it. Our main editorial and business offices were on the twenty-sixth floor, which was as high as the elevators went, but Ralph and I shared a kind of penthouse office on the twenty-ninth floor which could only be reached by a very narrow, very steep, circular iron staircase. Ralph and I ran up and down that staircase between the twenty-sixth and twenty-ninth floors not less than fifty times a day. It wasn't so bad if you didn't look down.

The penthouse was nice, if monastic. There were two desks on a small square cement floor. There was an FM radio on a little table. There were about forty hanging plants. And there were huge windows on three sides. From the east windows you could see the East River. From the north ones you could see Central Park. And from the west ones you could see every ship on the docks of the Hudson. If the hours had been shorter and willing women more available, it wouldn't have been such a bad place to work.

Ralph Ginzburg has been called a number of things, including brilliant promoter, misguided muckraker and vulgar sensationalist. It is not my purpose here to either defend the man or attack him—I happen to like him—but—I think I can characterize him for you by relating one short anecdote.

We got a lot of hate mail at *Eros,* most of it hysterical in tone, most of it profane, and much of it anti-Semitic. It was very painful for me to read, and so every time I opened a letter to the editor and saw that the drift of it was shrill and demented, I simply flipped it into the wastebasket. Ralph caught me throwing away a hate letter one day and stopped me.

"Any time you get one that mentions either God or Christ," he said, "let me have it for the Bible File."

"The Bible File?" I said. "What the hell is the Bible File?"

"Well," said Ralph a little self-consciously, "the only way we manage to keep our heads above water here is to see that nothing ever goes to waste. I figure if we can get together a list of several thousand people who object to *Eros* on religious grounds, we can make up a special mailing and sell them Bibles."

One night after Ralph had gone home I heard footsteps clank slowly up the iron staircase. There was a pause and then a heavy knock. The hour was very late. The building was very empty. What manner of visitor awaited me on the other side of the door?

Another knock. Heavier.

I looked around for something to defend myself with, finally settling on an empty Coke bottle, and went to unlock the door.

There stood a uniformed cop.

"This *Eros* magazine?" he said.

That's what the foot-high letters said on the door I had just opened. There was no getting around it.

"Uh, yeah," I said.

"Who're you?" he said.

I put down the Coke bottle. "Me? Well, I'm, uh . . . work around here . . . sort of. . . ."

"What are you—janitor or something?"

"Janitor? Oh. Well, not really a janitor, no. I—"

"What's yer name?"

"My name?"

"Yeah, yer name."

"Oh. Greenburg."

"Greenburg? Say, wait a minute. Aren't you the publisher?"

"No. Oh no. *Ginzburg,* publisher is Ralph *Ginzburg.* I'm *Greenburg.*"

The cop studied my face for several moments, expecting perhaps that I would crack under the strain and change my story. At length he spoke.

"Who else is here?" he said.

"Nobody."

"You here alone?"

"Yes."

He looked around the small room.

"We got a call," he said, gazing thoughtfully out over the moonlit Hudson. "Somebody called and said there was funny stuff going on up here. That true?" he said, turning to face me again. "Any funny stuff going on up here, Ginzburg?"

"Greenburg. No, sir, no funny stuff."

"No fooling around? You know what I mean."

"What do you mean?"

"Women," he said. "You got any women up here?"

"No women up here," I said, trying to stop a smile.

"What's so goddam funny?"

"Nothing, sir. No women. You can take a look around if you don't believe me."

He walked around, looked under the desks, behind the plants, in the filing cabinets and in the wastebaskets.

"You sure there's no women around here?"

"Trust me," I said.

He poked around a little more, then opened the door and turned to go. "We know you got them up here somewhere," he said. "And sooner or later we'll find them—don't worry, Ginzburg."

"I won't," I said.

He left.

The weeks slipped by without my having so much as a coffee date. It was now late November. My horniness and my preoccupation with meeting eligible women had gotten so bad they found their way into every conversation I had with Ralph about the magazine. Finally he decided to take pity on me.

"When's Thanksgiving—next Thursday?" he said.

"Yeah."

"Tell you what," he said. "The night before Thanksgiving we'll have a party here. What do you say? Booze, dancing, girls, the works. What do you say?"

"I'll believe it when I see it," I said.

"Don't worry," he said. "Just a few more days of work and then we'll really have some fun."

The day of the Thanksgiving party arrived. From lunch on, I couldn't keep my mind on my work.

Promptly at four-thirty Ralph stood up, unplugged the FM radio, put it under his arm and opened the door. "C'mon," he said. "Party time."

I followed him down to the twenty-sixth floor.

There, party preparations were already in full swing. The bookkeeper had unlocked a special closet and produced a bottle of bourbon and a bottle of scotch, the officer manager had sent down for ice cubes and paper cups, and before I knew it, Ralph had plugged in the FM radio and four couples from the business office were waltzing gaily around the filing cabinets to the strains of Toccata and Fugue in D Minor by Bach.

By five-fifteen the dancing couples had been reduced to one, the music was the largo from *Death and Transfiguration,* and three elderly ladies from the subscription department had had too much bourbon and couldn't stop giggling.

Promptly at five-thirty the heaviest of the giggling ladies threw up, the other two helped her to the rest room and everybody else went home.

Ralph and I went back upstairs to work.

"My God," I said, tousling my hair in mock abandon, "are all *Eros* office parties this wild?"

"Okay, so it was a lousy party," said Ralph. "Big deal. Big goddam deal." He began to type. "Okay," he said, swiveling around in his chair, "tell you what. Next week we'll have a better one. A real one. I'll invite some terrific models I know. We'll really pull out all the stops. It'll be a real bash. Okay? What do you say?"

"Models?" I said.

"The most luscious models in the business."

"A real honest-to-God party?"

127

"A regular barn-burner. C'mon, what do you say?"

"Well . . . sure. It sounds great."

"Good," he said. "Meanwhile, let's get back to work. We've already wasted an hour and a half."

On Thanksgiving Day I called my folks in Chicago.

"Where are you calling from?" said my father.

"Here."

"Here? Where's here?" said my mother.

"At the office."

"At the office? On Thanksgiving Day? Where are you going for Thanksgiving Dinner?"

"I've already been."

"Where?"

"Ralph and I ran out and had a pizza."

"A pizza? On Thanksgiving Day?"

"Well, we're very busy."

"You're very busy? You'll end up in the hospital from overwork. Then you won't be very busy."

"We just didn't have time for a big dinner, is all, Mom. Listen, did you get the issue of *Eros* I sent you? The one with my story in it?"

Pause.

"Yes."

"Oh. Good. How did you like it?"

Pause.

"It was nice," said my father. "Your story was very nice."

"Oh. Good. But the magazine . . . ?"

Pause.

128

"Listen," said my mother. "What would you prefer that we tell them?"

"Tell whom?"

"Our friends. When they ask."

"When they ask what?"

"When they ask where you're working."

"You mean you haven't told them?"

"We wanted to talk to you first."

"Why can't you tell them the truth? I'm working at *Eros* magazine."

Another pause.

"Listen," said my mother, "neither your father nor I have ever held you back. Whatever you have wanted to do in the past has always been all right with us."

"I know that," I said. "So what?"

"Leaving Chicago, moving to California, throwing a wonderful education in industrial design and a Master of Arts degree right out the window to go into the field of advertising, then *leaving* California and advertising to go to New York—we never held you back."

"I know that," I said. "So what?"

Yet another pause.

"Suppose that we just tell our friends that you are doing something in the general field of publishing," she said.

"Tell them whatever you like," I sighed.

Ralph and I decided our image at *Eros* sorely needed upgrading. We had an idea. We knew that Salvador Dali was currently in New York at the

St. Regis Hotel. We knew he was preoccupied by various forms of kinky sex. We would get him to do an entire portfolio of original erotic artwork for us.

We met Dali one Sunday afternoon in the King Cole Bar of the St. Regis—a dapper gentleman in a pin-striped suit, a gold brocade vest, a horribly twisted black knit tie, a sturdy silverheaded cane and, of course, the well-known waxed mustache.

Dali, who undoubtedly knew English as well as either of us, appeared to have great trouble understanding what we wanted from him, breaking into irrelevant rambling discourses in which he referred to himself in the third person and sprinkled an otherwise English vocabulary with French prepositions and definite articles.

"Dali weesh to comprehend *le* substance of what you say," he said. "But *le* mind of Dali ees not posseeble to grasp *le* essence of *le* conception. Een any case, Dali ees fortunate to have *avec* heem *le* most fontosteec book een *le* entire world, from wheech he weel create for you *le* most fontosteec article."

"You want to . . . *write* for us?" said Ralph.

Dali nodded. "Dali ees not only *le* most fontosteec genius of all *les* graphic arts, he ees also *le* most fontosteec writer *dans le* entire universe. Thees," he said, placing before us the book which he had been holding, "ees *le* research *pour le* article Dali weesh to write for you."

The book was French. After deciphering a few key words in the title, I realized that it was also scatological. Then Dali announced what subject he wished to treat in his article for us: the erotic aspects of breaking wind.

It wasn't quite what we'd had in mind somehow. On the other hand, could we pass up a chance to have Salvador Dali as an *Eros* contributor? Ralph and I held a hurried conference in whispers.

"What do you think?" he said.

"I don't know," I said.

"We've handled controversial stuff before," he said.

"Yeah, but nothing quite in this vein."

"I know," he said. "Listen, it'll have Dali's byline. Maybe that'll insulate us from the subject matter."

"Maybe," I said.

"Let's do it," he said. "What the hell."

"What the hell," I said.

"Okay," said Ralph to Dali, "you're on. You write us the article and we'll give you a thousand dollars."

Once more *le* mind of Dali did not comprehend. He wrote on the tablecloth the figure he thought we meant: a one followed by five zeros. Ralph crossed off two of the zeros. Dali shrugged. Then he nodded.

"Le article weel be finished een two weeks," he said. "Eet weel be fontosteec."

We left Dali in the King Cole Bar. Ralph went off to another appointment and I returned to the office. Shortly after I reached my desk the phone rang. Normally we didn't answer the phone on

Sundays. We felt that anybody who expected a magazine office to be open on Sundays was not the sort of person we'd be interested in talking to. However, I had just been musing about how horny I was and I wasn't thinking very rationally, so I picked up the phone.

"Is this *Eros* magazine?" said a delicious feminine voice.

"Why, yes," I said.

"Who am I speaking to, please?"

Normally, to spare myself involvement with irate subscribers, I said I was the floor polisher.

"This is the managing editor," I said.

"Oh," she said. "Well, I've just been looking through your magazine and I wanted to tell you how lovely it is."

"Well, thank you very much," I said.

"Personally, I don't read magazines of this type," she said with obvious embarrassment, "but yours was so attractively designed and so tastefully written that I wasn't the slightest bit offended."

"That's very kind of you," I said. "Tell me, who am I speaking to?"

"Would you like to know what I'm wearing now?" she said.

"Uh . . . what?"

"Can you guess what I'm wearing?"

"No," I said, "what are you wearing?"

"Just my brassiere and panties," she said.

"I see," I said.

"Did you hear that noise just then?" she said.

"Uh, no, look, I—"

"That was my husband. He's trying to take off my brassiere and I'm not letting him. That was the elastic you heard snapping."

"I see," I said. "Look, I'm not really in such great shape to hear any more of—"

"Did you hear *that* noise?" she said.

"No. Look, I—"

"He just ripped off my panties."

There were a lot of scuffling and giggling noises. It is not altogether clear to me why I did not hang up the phone. Total paralysis may have been one explanation.

"Are you still there, sir?" she said.

"Yeah," I said dully.

"Do you know what he's"—gasp—"doing to me now?"

"No," I said, "I don't."

In exceedingly graphic terms, she told me.

Four days later we had another office party. Ralph's luscious models were mysteriously absent. Present were the same bookkeeper, bourbon and paper cups and personnel as before. The same four couples waltzed to Bach. The same three elderly ladies drank too much and couldn't stop giggling. The only difference was that it took fifteen minutes longer for the one who had thrown up last time to go into her act.

When the party finally broke up at seven o'clock, I myself was feeling queasy and a little faint.

"Go on home," said Ralph. "Knock off early for once, what the hell."

I went home and took my temperature. I had fever and I was feeling very dizzy and nauseous and peculiar. I telephoned a doctor I knew and described my symptoms. He agreed to come over and have a look at me.

His examination was brief.

"What do you think?" I said as he regarded me in a parody of doctor poses—lips pursed, brow furrowed, fingers tented.

"I think maybe mononucleosis. Maybe infectious hepatitis."

He was two thirds right. I had mono, hepatitis and jaundice.

I checked into Doctors Hospital, which may be one of the fanciest hospitals in New York but which looks like a once elegant hotel gone to seed. The receptionist gave me a professional once-over and demanded payment of a hundred and fifty dollars in advance. Luckily, I'd brought my checkbook.

They put me in a private room and, although I was wildly nauseous, they insisted that I eat to keep my strength up. I tried to eat and couldn't. They said that if I didn't eat they'd have to feed me intravenously. I panicked. As a child, the only thing that my mother could ever do to get me to eat when I was particularly unhungry was to threaten me with intravenous feeding. I promised the doctors I would eat. But I simply couldn't get any food past my lips. So they brought in the intravenous bottles and tubes and I thought I was going to pass out from my childhood horror of what was about to be done to me.

Like most childhood horrors, intravenous feeding turned out to be nothing but a mild annoyance. And within a few days, though I was still being fed through tubes in my arm, I was sitting up in bed, once more editing *Eros*.

Running a national magazine from a hospital bed is at best a tricky proposition. First of all, it's difficult to transform old nurses into copy boys. Second, it's hard to find time—what with normal daily hospital routines of temperature-takings, washing-ups, rubbing-downs, injections, bed-makings, and room-cleanings,—for more than fifty hours of work a week. Then too, your telephone cord keeps getting tangled up in your intravenous tubes.

I worried at times that I was overdoing it. But I loved the image I was creating. Why the doctors let me do it I have no idea.

Late one night I awoke with a throbbing headache. I pressed the night call button and in a moment the night nurse padded into my darkened room.

"What is it?" she whispered.

"A headache," I whispered. "Can I get some aspirins?"

"Sure," she said. She peered around the room at the stacks of papers and manuscripts and books. "Are you a lawyer?" she whispered.

"No, a magazine editor."

"Oh. What magazine?"

"*Eros.*"

"How do you spell that?"

She took out a pencil and a piece of paper which she carried for just such emergencies.

"How do I spell what?" I whispered.

"*Eros.*"

"Oh. E-r-o-s."

She dutifully wrote it down. "What is the address?" she whispered.

"What?"

"The address."

"Oh. 110 West Fortieth Street."

She wrote that down too. "I wish you great success," she whispered.

"Thanks. Listen, how about those aspirins?"

"Right," she whispered and padded out the door. A moment later she was back with the pills. "My son is a structural engineer," she whispered.

"I see."

"He makes seven hundred dollars a day."

"I see."

"He lives in Algeria."

"Oh."

"He married a little Jewess and they're very happy together."

"Good."

"Are you Jewish?"

"Yes."

"Do you keep the Sabbath?"

"No."

136

"Where is your mother?"

"Chicago."

"Write her," she said and disappeared.

That is a verbatim transcript. I know because I turned on the light and wrote it down, headache notwithstanding.

After three weeks in the hospital I was allowed to return to my apartment and recuperate.

Meanwhile, at the office, Dali had finally sent in his completed manuscript. Unfortunately, most of the words in the piece, though English, were unknown to us. And the article itself, to gently understate the case, was not quite readable.

The main condition under which I was permitted to leave the hospital was that I remain in bed in my apartment for three more weeks. Ralph sent six cartons of foreign pornographic material over for me to sort through for possible inclusion in the magazine. There was pornography from every nation in the world. Sorting through it was at first diverting, but by the second or third day it began to take on a tiresome sameness. One nation's pornography is almost identical to the next's. In fact, the only variations I noted were that the Germans seem to consider defecation in all forms a communal romantic act, and the Japanese get a terrific giggle out of men whose organs are so large that they have to cart them around in a wheelbarrow.

On the first Monday back in my apartment, my

laundryman was to make me realize the irony of continuing to work for *Eros*. He dropped by as I was emptying the laundry hamper. I'd never been at home when he picked up and delivered the laundry before, so this was our first meeting. After a pleasant exchange of greetings, I excused myself and went back to the hamper.

"I'll only be a minute," I called from the bathroom. "Sit down and look at a magazine or something."

"Take your time, take your time," he said.

When I reappeared with the laundry, I found him studying the latest issue of *Eros* so intently he hardly noticed me.

"Sorry to have kept you waiting," I said.

"Take your time, take your time," he said, never lifting his eyes from the page.

"What do you think of the magazine?" I said.

"Personally, I don't go in for stuff like this," he said. "I got to admit, however, that it holds my interest. Where'd you get this?"

"I work there," I said.

"Don't you wish," he said.

"No, really. I'm the managing editor."

"You're putting me on."

"Honest. Here, check the masthead. See?" I pointed to my name in the masthead.

He looked first at me, then at the name, then back at me—hoping perhaps to detect some family resemblance.

"Now do you believe me?" I said.

"Yeah," he said. "Listen. What's it like, working up there?"

I shrugged. "Like working any place else, I guess."

"No, really. What's it like?" he said, warming to the subject. "Tell me about the orgies."

"There aren't any."

"Come on," he said. "Who am I gonna tell?"

"Honest. No orgies."

"Aw. Not even a few wild office parties?"

"Nope. Not unless waltzing around filing cabinets to an FM radio and drinking bourbon out of a paper cup and watching elderly ladies throw up is your idea of a wild office party."

"Aww."

He was beginning to get depressed. I could tell. I had really let him down.

And then it hit me: if my laundryman was getting depressed just to be *hearing* about it, how much more depressed was I to be *living* it! That *Eros* had not improved my sex life was regrettable. That it had occupied so much of my time as to destroy it entirely was intolerable. The time had come to quit. And the man who'd made me realize it was already halfway out the door with my dirty laundry. I couldn't let him leave like this, not after all he'd done for me.

"Listen," I said, "I changed my mind. If you give me your solemn word of honor not to repeat a single word of this, I'll tell you what it was really like up at *Eros*."

He turned to face me. "I promise," he said. "On my mother's head."

"Then sit down."

He sat down.

I told him quite a story.

15

I recuperated enough to contemplate brief forays out of my apartment.

Because of the hepatitis damage to my liver the doctors had forbidden mè to drink any alcoholic beverages for a period of six months. So of course liquor became an obsession to me. Every evening I slunk down to the corner package store and purchased a miniature bottle of some exotic liqueur distilled from apricots, cherries, bananas, artichokes, marsh grass or jujubes and spirited it back to my apartment. There I would uncork it, inhale it, nearly pass out from the forbidden fragrance. Then I'd place it lovingly on the shelf in anticipation of the day my own personal Prohibition would be repealed. I even went so far as to design an upright bar and have it custom carpentered to house my growing cache of liquor.

In a heated telephone conversation with Ginzburg over editorial policy I finally resigned my job at *Eros*. But the moment I hung up the phone I fell apart. Without *Eros* I had neither friends nor income, and I was badly in need of both. I experienced twenty minutes of blind panic, during which I placed long-distance calls to everyone I knew across the country: to Burt in Los Angeles, to my parents in Chicago, to I no longer remember whom. Curiously, every single one of the people I called was out.

I sat down and tried to pull myself together. To return to Los Angeles or Chicago seemed an even worse idea than staying on in New York. I had a lease on an apartment, continuing treatment from the doctors who'd pulled me through mono and hepatitis, and besides I couldn't bear another move or an implicit admission that I had failed to make it in the Big Apple.

It was clear that I was going to stay in New York, at least for a while, and to do so I had to get another high-paying job immediately. I knew that my best chance for such a position was in the field of advertising. I took out my old Los Angeles portfolio of ads and looked it over. I rearranged it, took out the weaker ads, updated my résumé and then went to the Classified Directory. I copied down the name and address of every advertising agency in the Yellow Pages that I'd ever heard of. I composed a short letter of introduction to go with my résumé, saying I would telephone soon for an appointment. And then I spent the next several hours typing up résumés and cover letters to the fifty or so ad agencies on my list. By the time I returned from mailing them, I was in control again.

In the next three weeks I developed such an insane fear of people that I was terrified of answer-

ing the doorbell or the telephone or of even passing
strangers on the street, yet I managed somehow to
brazen my way through a few dozen interviews
with condescending creative directors and bullying
agency presidents. Don't ask me how someone
could on the one hand be pathologically afraid of
answering the telephone and on the other hand be
aggressive with agency presidents. Probably it had
to do with the endless hours of practice I'd had
yelling at MacNish. In any case, ad agency presidents are the one group of people I not only don't
fear but almost get a kick out of playing games
with. Before long I had a copy-writing job at one
of the larger creative agencies. I was shocked to
discover they were willing to pay me even more
than I was earning at *Eros,* yet expected me to work
a paltry forty hours a week.

I was able to keep my terror of people well
enough in check to function at the office, but I
was still wholly unable to eat lunch or dinner with
anyone, particularly a woman, without being overcome by waves of nausea. I concocted elaborate
excuses for dining alone. Finally I located a reputable psychoanalyst and began seeing him five
times a week.

They say that when you begin analysis your
most flagrant symptoms are the first to go. They
are right. After only a few weeks of treatment my
insane fear of people subsided to a sort of gentle
paranoia, and I was once more able to dine with
people, even women, without fearing that any moment I was going to puke my guts out.

I was a dutiful analysand, conscientiously waking in the middle of the night to scribble synopses of dreams on my bedside note pad, the better to spew them forth the following day on the analytic couch. I developed an agonizingly candid approach toward the doctor, which turned out to be merely a defense against *real* candor. I complained bitterly that the doctor, a Freudian, didn't talk to me, didn't answer my questions, and he in turn pointed out to me that I seldom gave him the opportunity. I developed a trick of relating a dream or incident and then trying to beat him to the analytic punch, interpreting it in its most unflattering light, feeling that I could face any possibility within myself—from latent homosexuality to murderous feelings toward my parents to God knows what —if only I, rather than the shrink, could be the first to name it. (It is at once striking and commonplace that the humiliating things I have been confessing here so easily took me months to tell the shrink—once bared, they no longer hold any special embarrassment for me.)

I became a master at finding sophisticated rebuttals to the few observations the good doctor did allow himself to voice. The neurotic game that Eric Berne labeled "Yes, But . . ." became in my cunning hands a game of "Aha! But . . ." Did the shrink point out that coming late to one's analytic session was the manifestation of Hostility Toward the Analyst? *Aha!* An interesting and possibly even valid point, *but* today it doesn't apply because it happens I left the house in plenty of time, and

144

it's only because the cab got stuck in crosstown traffic due to the collapse of a crane on Second Avenue and Forty-sixth Street that I was late.

And yet somehow my psychoanalysis progressed in spite of me. I managed to dredge up undredgeable fears and feelings to tell the shrink and I generally found them to be more banal than horrifying: as with the monster in *The Thing,* you go through practically the whole movie in terror of confronting It, and when you finally do It turns out to be only James Arness in a funny suit.

I decided that the masks we all wear, rather than being protective disguises which conceal the real us, are all really us. And that we are vulnerable through every one of them—vulnerable not only to the hurtful remark of a qualified critic but even to the impersonal insult of a random crank on the street: "Hmmmmm," I muse after the latter, "maybe he's got a point there." My opinion of myself at any given moment is heavily influenced by the last thing I've heard said about me, no matter whether it's been said by a dear friend or a crazy person. And when the last thing said happens to be a deliberate insult, I tend to take a wee bit longer than most people to think up a snappy rejoinder. With me it's not a matter of brooding about it for an hour or so and then coming up with a brilliant I-should-have-said. There are things people have said to me five and six years ago that I'm still working on. ("You probably don't remember me, but in summer of '66 we were at this cocktail party, and I'd just like to comment on something

145

you said to me then.")

I began to see that the most pernicious force in my life was guilt. At *Eros* I had whimsically created a fictitious character in our billing department named "Moms" Mulvaney to write guilt-provoking letters to subscribers who had failed to pay their bills, renew their subscriptions, whatever. The responses from the Moms Mulvaney letters were always about six times greater than any other type of pitch we tried, which led me to suspect that I was not the only mother's son in the world who'd been programed to respond to guilt. Using this theme, I began writing a book called *How to Be a Jewish Mother*.

Meanwhile, my liver had repaired itself and I was mercifully permitted to stop sniffing and start sipping liquor again. And once I was allowed to resume drinking I found myself again able to muster the courage to go to parties and resume meeting girls.

16

One of the first real parties I went to in New York was at the spare, antique-and-chrome apartment of a new art director friend I'd met at the agency. About midnight, into the party walked one of the cockiest young men and the sexiest little girl I had ever seen in my life.

The guy, who lived on the floor above the art director, was some kind of entrepreneur who was involved in a lot of big deals which, if they had been half as big as he said they were, would have made us all familiar with his name today, and we aren't. The girl, whose name was Shelley, was a teenager with incredibly long straight black hair which reached to the bottom of her bouncy little buttocks. She had on high leather boots that ended just above her knees and a short leather skirt that almost succeeded in reaching the crotch of her perky pink panties.

I supposed I gaped at her rather transparently, because she returned my gaze with a moist, somewhat amused smile. I had never desired anyone so immediately or so powerfully in my life, never before wanted to abandon myself so completely to nakedness and rubbing things and wet, licking, sucking, whimpering, mindless fucking things. I loved her with mind and heart and body and I would cheerfully have written out a proposal of marriage to her on the spot in exchange for even one night in bed with her. So what I did was I went into another room of the apartment and hid.

My host the art director found me cowering in the other room and asked me what was wrong. When I told him he chuckled. He insisted I come out and meet the cocky entrepreneur and his moist, leather-bound teenager, and though I was truly terrified I let myself be dragged back over to them and I mumbled some facsimile of greeting.

There was no big secret about what I was feeling. My forehead was a small rear-projection screen on which were flickering the depraved blue-movie fantasies of my mind. I was so obvious and pathetic that everyone was very solicitous of me, finally guiding me into a chair and bringing me enormous quantities of alcohol to relieve my nervousness.

The entrepreneur, whose name was Cliff, had brought down several joints of pot which he generously distributed among the guests, and when he came over to where I was sitting he winked and said:

"What do you think of Shelley?"

"I don't guess that's much of a secret," I said. "I think she's sensational."

"Great-looking chick, huh?"

"Sensational," I said.

"You want her number?" he said.

"Shelley's?" I said.

He nodded.

"Why?" I said. "I mean, I don't understand—aren't you two going together or something?"

"*Going* together?" he said. "I don't *go* with anybody, man. I've got too many chicks to *go* with any of them. In fact I'm splitting soon because I've got another chick coming by upstairs in about twenty minutes. Why don't you take Shelley's number, though? She's kind of young, but she's lots of fun. I think you'd like her."

"I'm sure I would," I said.

He scribbled a number on the inside of a matchbook and handed it to me. I thanked him and put it away in my pocket, wondering if I'd ever have the guts to call her, and then Cliff left for his next date upstairs.

I thought about Shelley a good deal in the days that followed, and once or twice I even got as far as dialing the first two digits of her number. But then I'd chicken out and hang up the phone, resolving to go through with it when I had gotten back some of the self-confidence I'd lost in Europe.

The weeks passed, and then the months. Spring came to New York and the little piles of charcoal-gray snow and dog shit melted away and were replaced by tender young shoots of green grass and dog shit. I'd put on some weight and regained enough confidence to at least start going out with girls again.

149

I enrolled in a judo course at the Y.M.C.A., feeling it was high time I became a one-man tactical police force, able to protect his women from violence on the streets. But the judo instructor was a huge Negro who spotted me as an instant scapegoat and started using me exclusively to demonstrate all the throws. I limped around in pain for about eight weeks and then I quit the class. I figured I could always buy my women little purse-sized atomizers of Mace.

I had finished *How to Be a Jewish Mother*, found a publisher, and before I knew it the book was not only in the bookstores but on the best-seller list. Since it was the first book I'd ever written, I concluded it was insanely easy to write a best seller. I quit advertising to become a free-lance writer.

I considered moving back to Los Angeles, which was cleaner, friendlier, prettier and more comfortable than New York. But I had discovered I was an ambitious, competitive person, and I feared that if I returned to California the limits of my ambitions would shrink to things like developing a really sensational tan, and that somewhere along the way my brain would turn to Franco-American macaroni. So I merely moved to a larger and more interesting-looking apartment.

One afternoon I was lying around my cozy new place and I got to thinking about old Shelley and her preposterous overripe teenaged body, and I again fiddled with the possibility of calling her. My usual tight-assed, hung-up operating procedure would have been to phone her on a Tuesday night for a date the following Friday or Saturday, and I knew if I came on like that she wouldn't go out with me. But what if I tried to come on like the kind of guys she was used to? Guys like old Cliff with his offhand dates upstairs every twenty minutes?

Before I had enough time to think about it and get too nervous to go through with it I found the matchbook with her number on it and dialed and convinced myself I was, if not quite Cliff, at least somewhat Cliff-like.

The phone rang a few times and then Shelley's husky, incredibly sexy voice said hello, and I clung tightly to the image of Cliff. I told her my name and that Cliff had given me her number and I resisted the impulse to say: "You probably don't remember me, but . . ."

"Hey, wow," she said, "Cliff told me he gave you my number. Like I was wondering how long it would take you to get around to calling me."

That really knocked me out, but I concentrated hard on who I was trying to be, and after some idle chitchat I said I thought we ought to get together. She said she'd like to—when? I fought off the temptation to say: "How about next Saturday night?" and instead I said:

"How about right now?"

"Groovy," she said.

I gave her my address and told her how to get there. I had never before dared suggest that a girl come over to my house without picking her up and bringing her there, but she seemed to feel it was the most natural request in the world. She said she'd be over in about twenty minutes. *Twenty minutes!*

I hung up the phone and had a moment of panic. Talking on the telephone to a teenaged sex bomb and making that work was one thing. But what about when it came time to actually hop in the sack with her? It had been nearly a year since I'd made love to a woman by now—what if I didn't remember how?

I ran around the apartment, straightening it up. I put on the soft lights, some rock music, and changed into some calculatingly casual clothes. I shaved, brushed my teeth about six times, rolled on some deodorant, rinsed my mouth with mouthwash and slapped some great French shaving lotion on my face before I realized that I was doing it all wrong—kids Shelley's age valued honest, natural body smells, not phony perfumey lotions. I tried washing off all the shaving lotion and the deodorant, but it was hopeless. I stank of goodness. The doorbell rang. After checking myself in the mirror for the fortieth time and rumpling my hair, I casually shuffled to the door and opened it.

There she was, still wearing her absurdly short leather skirt and her astonishingly high leather boots and her outrageously unfair teenaged body, obviously not having changed clothes or grown a day older in the months since the party—as though she had been created strictly for my use and had no other life when she was not in my presence. Her

lips were still moist and inviting and mildly mock-
ing. Her straight black hair still hung down to the
base of her bitable tushy. She was so succulent and
juicy and wonderful I wanted to cry. I ushered her
into the apartment.

"Oh wow," she said looking around, "oh wow.
You live here alone?"

"Uh, yeah."

She appeared to be fairly impressed with the
place and I figured I was a step ahead. It really was
a terrific-looking apartment: a duplex with two
small rooms upstairs and one large bedroom downstairs that opened out onto a patio and a two-level
forty-foot-deep garden. I'd planted the garden
myself with long grasses, flowers and shrubbery,
and I'd sunk green floodlights into the ground under the trees—now in all their Southern California
glory since it was nearly dark out. Inside the apartment was the custom-made bar I'd designed, lots of
walnut paneling and indirect lighting—Hugh Hef-
ner would have been proud.

Shelley sat down and I offered her a drink, instantly losing several points in the process. She
didn't drink, of course—no kids drank these days,
if only I'd paused to think before I spoke—instead
she pulled out a couple of joints and offered me
one. I accepted, knowing that although I was no
stranger to marijuana, knowing that although I'd
been introduced to it about the time she was in
second grade, she would still look at the way I was
smoking it and decide I was doing it wrong.

We smoked awhile in a silence which I found uncomfortable but which didn't seem to bother her at all.

"This is pretty good stuff," I said at last.

"Yeah."

"Yeah," I said. "So tell me. What'd you do to-day?"

"Nothing."

"Nothing?"

"Well, you know. Stuff for school."

"Yeah. Where do you go?" I said.

"To school?"

"Yeah."

"Julia Richman."

"Julia Richman the, uh, high school," I said.

"Yeah."

I had a sudden vision of her dressed in a pinafore and pigtails, licking a lollipop, playing on a playground swing, and me dressed as a bummy, dirty old man walking up and offering her a slug of whiskey.

"How *is* Julia Richman?" I said. "As a, you know, school, I mean."

"Oh wow," she said.

I waited for some further amplification but none appeared to be forthcoming. "Yeah," I said finally.

"It's actually not that bad of a place to score, though," she said.

"To . . . score. To buy drugs, you mean."

"Yeah."

"What can you, uh, score there?"

"Oh, you know. Anything. Grass, hash, speed, coke. Anything."

"Acid?" I said.

"Yeah."

"Have you had acid?" I said.

"Today, you mean?"

"No, I meant . . ."

"Ever?"

"Yeah."

"Well, sure," she said.

"Oh."

"The only thing I haven't really tried," she said, "is smack."

"Heroin."

"Yeah."

"Well, I don't blame you," I said. "I mean, that stuff can really be dangerous."

"Yeah," she said, "I'd be scared to take it more than once."

I laughed. *"I'd* be scared to even take it *once,"* I said.

"Oh, it's not so bad if you only take it once," she said.

"How do you know?"

"Well, you know. I mean, like I didn't notice any bad effects."

I looked at her carefully. "You mean you've taken heroin?" I said.

"Only once," she said.

"I thought you just said you'd never tried it."

"Well, wow. Once isn't anything. It's when you do it all the time."

"I see," I said. "But isn't that, uh, dangerous? I mean isn't it, you know, habit-forming?"

"Not if you only do it a couple of times like I did," she said.

I decided not to push it. My purpose, after all, was not to get her to lead a clean life, my purpose was to get my dirty old man self into those warm sweet panties of hers.

"Tell me," I said with elaborate nonchalance, "how old are you?"

"Me?"

"Yes."

"Seventeen," she said.

"Seventeen," I said.

"Pretty much," she said.

"Pretty much?"

"Well, I mean I will be in a couple of weeks."

"Ah."

"How old are *you?*" she said.

"Me?" I said.

"Yeah."

"Nearly thirty," I said.

Now it was *her* turn to be elaborately nonchalant. "Thirty . . . years old," she said.

"Yes," I said. "Nearly." I was actually still a good two years away from it, but had already begun despondently thinking of myself as Nearly Thirty. Shelley soberly contemplated the piece of news I had given her.

"I knew someone who had a thing with someone your age once," she said finally.

"Imagine that," I said.

"Yeah," she said. "What do you do, work?"

"Yes."

"Oh yeah? Where?"

"Right here at home. I'm a free-lance writer."

"Yeah? What do you write?"

"Oh, books, plays, screen plays, magazine articles. You know."

This type of conversation was clearly not going to lead to anything sexual, and I was getting rather restless. Also, joint or no joint, I still needed a drink. I stood up.

"You sure I can't get you anything to drink?" I said.

"I don't know. Are you going to have something?"

"Well, yeah. I thought I would."

"Okay, then maybe I'll have something. What've you got?"

I smiled proudly. "Just about anything you can name," I said. "What would you like?"

"Pear brandy," she said.

"Pear brandy?"

"Yeah."

"I'm sorry," I said. "Pear brandy happens to be about the one thing I don't have. Is there anything else that you'd like?"

She shrugged. "I don't care. Whatever you have."

I went over to the bar, poured myself a scotch on the rocks and her a vodka on the rocks and returned to the couch. I handed her the drink and sat down next to her and tried to plot out the least awkward way of making my move. It was clear to me that to have gotten her over to my apartment and spent all this time with her and then *not* make a pass at her would blow my chance with her completely. After trying for another half hour to think of a natural-looking way of getting started, I finally just leaned over and attached my mouth to hers, catching her in mid-sentence, and then her lips opened and our tongues touched and I was in heaven.

I kissed her and caressed her firm young wonderful body through her clothes, and I had to concentrate hard on not blurting out terrible uncool love and marriage things. I think she was enjoying what we were doing, but it was hard for me to tell since I was so excited myself. I managed to take off her heavy sweater and her leather skirt without excessive clumsiness, and then I hoarsely suggested it might be more comfortable if we went downstairs.

We walked downstairs in our absolute underwear and as we walked I prayed: Please, God, please—let me do all right and not puke or be impotent or forget what part goes where—please let me fuck this child, please just let me shove my nasty old shlong into this teenaged child's warm little pussy and please let me do all right, and then after that You can do anything You want with me —but please, God, don't let me get this close to ecstasy without letting me have it.

We sat down on my new king-sized bed. I took

off her underwear and her boots and then I climbed on top of her and inside of her and it was *marvelous*—just absolutely incredibly *marvelous*—and, mercifully, I hadn't forgotten how to do it. I don't think my performance was anything more than competent, having put away all that liquor and everything, but I wasn't too bad either, and in the moment of orgasm I would cheerfully have converted to Catholicism on the off chance that the God I'd been dealing with hadn't been Jewish.

We lay together for a while and then we got up and went into the bathroom and took a shower together. I kissed her and hugged her a lot in the shower, and when we came out and toweled our bodies dry she had somehow changed. With her make-up washed off and with her marvelous long hair all wet and without her clothes on she looked about twelve years old. I became really nervous, having screwed someone who looked so young, and I fought off my guilt with thoughts of her drug experiences and her sex experiences with guys like Cliff.

She said she'd better be getting home soon or her mother would worry (I really needed hearing about worried mothers at that point), so we got dressed and went out looking for a cab to take her home. She held my hand all the way back to her house in the cab, and her super-cool drugsy manner of speech, I noticed with considerable surprise, had lapsed into some dimly remembered thing out of my past. What it was, I realized, was the kind of coy, cutesy, self-conscious way of talking that teenagers talked when *I* was in high school.

We arrived at her house and I opened the door of the cab to let her out, but she asked if I would mind letting the cab go and coming inside to meet her mother. I wasn't at all anxious to meet her mother, but I nodded dully and paid the cabby. As we walked up to her door she said:

"I hope you don't think I do that all the time."

"What do you mean?" I said. I thought maybe she meant asking me to let the cab go and coming inside to meet her mother.

"I mean like what we just got done doing," she said, somewhat embarrassed.

"You mean making love?" I said.

She nodded.

"You mean you don't usually go to bed with a guy the first time you see him or what?"

She appeared truly hurt. "I've only balled like two other guys in my *life*," she said, "and only after going steady with them for like *years*."

"Come on, Shelley," I said gently, "you mean to tell me you went steady for years with *Cliff?*"

"*Cliff!*" she said. "Oh wow, I never balled *Cliff*."

"You didn't?"

"No. I mean he *wanted* me to, but I wouldn't. Why?" she said, "did he tell you he balled me?"

"Not exactly," I said. "I just assumed he had. I mean, I thought you were a big swinger and everything or I probably wouldn't even have made a move at you till about the fourth or fifth date."

"Oh wow," she said. "The only reason I went along with it was I thought *you* were a big swinger, and if I didn't I'd never see you again."

We looked at each other for a long moment, and then we went inside to meet her mother. In a kind of wacky way, I knew I was back in high school and had somehow agreed to go steady.

Shelley's mom, Mrs. Robish, greeted us at the door. She was a voluptuous woman in her early forties, plumper than you would have wished, but not bad-looking. She was a seductive blonde and spoke with what I took to be a Polish accent.

"Well," said Mrs. Robish, looking me over, "so this is your young man, Shelley?"

"Yeah," said Shelley and perfunctorily introduced us.

I shook hands with Mrs. Robish, figuring it was the continental thing to do, and she seemed reluctant to let go of me.

"He's very cute, your young man, Shelley," said Mrs. Robish, "*very* cute."

I smiled wanly and Mrs. Robish continued holding my hand.

"You better watch out, Shelley, that I don't take your young man away from you," said Mrs. Robish.

At that point a greasy-looking foreign man maybe thirty years old, maybe less, entered the room. He had a skinny mustache, a luminescent suit and an even heavier accent than Mrs. Robish.

"Ah," said Mrs. Robish, spying the guy, "here is Maurice. Maurice, say hello to Mr. Greenburg."

Maurice did a little bow and shook hands with me. "Meestair Grinnboorg, a great plaisir," he said. "Gude evening, Shelley," he said to Shelley.

"Maurice and I are engaged to marry," said Mrs. Robish.

"Oh," I said. "Well, congratulations."

"Just now," said Mrs. Robish, "we are only lovers."

"Ah," I said.

"Perhaps you will stay to supper, Mr. Greenburg," said Mrs. Robish.

"Oh no, no, thanks," I said. "I have to be going."

"Yes? But there is much food. Too much for the three of us. Perhaps you will stay and help us dispose of it?"

"Oh, that's very kind of you," I said, "but no, I'm afraid I have to run."

"Yes?" said Mrs. Robish. "Where must you run?"

"*Mom*, for God's sake," said Shelley.

"Where must you run, Mr. Greenburg?" said Mrs. Robish. "Another supper engagement?"

"Well no, not exactly," I said.

"Have you eaten yet this evening, Mr. Greenburg?" said Mrs. Robish.

"Well, no," I said, "but . . ."

Mrs. Robish took my hand again. "Then please," she said, "I insist you stay and eat with us. Unless our simple food would offend you?"

"*Offend* me," I said. "Of course not."

"Good," said Mrs. Robish. "Then you'll stay?"

"Well . . ."

There seemed to be no way of getting out of it without hurting foreign feelings.

"Excellent," said Mrs. Robish, giving my hand a big squeeze. "Maurice, get Mr. Greenburg a drink."

I was about to tell Maurice what to get me, but he only nodded and went off to fetch the drink. Mrs. Robish led me into the living room and seated me on the couch.

"Make yourself comfortable, Mr. Greenburg," she said. "Now I must go and cook, and Shelley must do some homework, but Maurice will entertain you until suppertime."

Mrs. Robish and Shelley went off to their respective tasks and Maurice came back into the room and handed me a large jelly glass full of yellow liquid with no ice in it. I took a sip of it and my eyes widened.

"What is this?" I said, my throat on fire.

"Please?"

I pointed to the glass. "This," I said. "What is it?"

"Ah. Pear brandy," said Maurice.

"Pear brandy," I said.

Maurice nodded. "It pleases you?" he said.

"Oh. Yes. Very good. Yes." I smiled. "Thank you."

Maurice smiled and sat down right next to me on the couch. I eyed him warily. He just sat there smiling at me. There was a lot of silence.

"So," I said, unable to stand the silence any longer. "Tell me. What do you do?"

"Please?"

"What do you do? What, uh, line are you in?"

"Ah. What I work?" he said.

"Yes."

"Ah." Maurice smiled his comprehension. "Fown-dation," he said.

"Fown-dation?" I said.

Maurice nodded.

"What *kind* of foundation—a charitable one?" I said.

"Please?"

"I say what *kind* of a foundation do you work for —a charitable one?"

Maurice shook his head impatiently. "Ghar-mens," he said.

"Ghar-mens?" I said blankly.

"Ghar-mens, *ghar*-mens," he said in exasperation. "Cower-sets, bras-heers, ghor-dles—to hawld opp de buttocks and de tits. Fown-dation *ghar*-mens."

"Foundation *gar*ments," I said. "Yes. I understand."

Maurice nodded his head impatiently and sighed. There was another longish silence.

"Well," I said, "that sounds very interesting. What do you do, sell them, fit them or what?"

Maurice nodded. "For Hess Klein," he said.

"For S. Klein the department store?"

"Hess Klein on de Sqvare. Ees how I meet Meeses Robeesh."

"Oh?"

"Feeting her for cower-sets. Lovely woman. Beeg bazooms. Lovely. You love beeg bazooms?"

"Uh, sure," I said. "I guess so."

"Beeg bazooms on Meeses Robeesh," he said. "I fall een love weeth them. Before the feeting ees

164

over we are proctically engaged."

"Well, that's very . . . sweet," I said.

"She make me very hoppy, that woman, weeth her beeg bazooms," he said. "I love them more than life."

"Tell me," I said, "how'd you happen to end up in that particular racket?"

"Please?"

"I say, how did you happen to wind up in the foundation garments game?"

"Ees not what you theenk," he said defensively.

"It's not."

"Eet's not that I am how you say 'torned on' by cower-sets, ghor-dles, bras-heers, oh no. Ees only to me a job. A profession. For avocations, for hobbies, I have other theengs."

"Ah."

"I am collector."

"Really?" I said. "What do you collect?"

"Oh, many theengs."

"Like what, for example?"

"Many theengs: ponties, staukeengs, gartair belts, theengs of thees natures. Linggery."

"Linggery. I see. Well, I'm glad to see you're so diversified in your interests."

"Deeversification ees my life. Do you know I have thairty-two separate varieties of ponties alone?"

"Imagine."

"Oh yes," said Maurice. He pointed a dramatic finger at me. "One of de three largest amateur collections een de entire United States of Americas!"

"Not really," I said. I began to look uncomfortably around. "Say, I wonder how we're doing on dinner in there," I said.

"Porhops sometimes you weesh to see my collection?" said Maurice.

"Uh, maybe so," I said, looking wildly around the room for some means of terminating our tête-à-tête. "Mrs. Robish," I called, "how are we doing in there?"

"Soup is on, everyone," she replied.

I was immensely relieved.

Two days later I got a greeting card in the mail. On the cover was a very cutesy little terrier with a peppy face and an envelope in his mouth. On the inside of the card was the following printed message:

> This little doggy came to say
> He hopes you have a happy day.
> If I weren't shy as shy can be,
> I'd be there now instead of he.
> —LOVE, SHELLEY.

I had my first real date with Shelley about a week after that. I took her out to dinner at a restaurant just like a grownup, and I couldn't completely get out of my head the image of Daddy taking his daughter out to eat. She had no idea what to order or how to eat it—things I had learned years before and then forgotten I'd had to learn them—and although I found it charming to be the teacher, it was still slightly disconcerting.

When I took her back to my apartment afterward, she let me neck with her but she stopped my hand before it had crept any farther up her leg than the top of her boot.

"What's the matter?" I said.

"Nothing."

"Then why did you stop me just now?"

"Because."

"Because what?"

"Because we're going too fast," she said.

"Too fast? Too fast for what?"

"Too fast for our second date," she said.

"But on our *first* date you went to *bed* with me."

"I know," she said, "but that was from a misunderstanding. It doesn't count."

"How could it not count? We went to bed together. We made love. I was inside of you. How could that not count?"

She sighed. "Oh wow," she said, then continued as if to a not very bright child. "It didn't count because we both thought it was something else. And also because . . ."

"And also because what?"

"Also because it wasn't important then," she said.

"And now it is?" I said.

She nodded, looking the other way. I was touched, but no less frustrated.

"Shelley honey," I said, taking her hands in mine, "that doesn't make any sense, does it—that it's okay to let a guy make love to you if he's not

167

important to you, and *not* to let him if he *is?*"

"I just don't want to give you the wrong idea about what kind of girl I am," she said, "that's all."

I let go of her hands and covered up my eyes. "I can't believe it," I said. "I just can't believe it. I'm practically thirty years old and I'm right back in high school. It's as if the last fifteen years never even happened. It's as if the whole sexual revolution never even happened."

I dropped my hands and looked at her. "Shelley," I said, "you're a sweet, lovely girl, a very sexual girl, and a very dear person. Making love to you was one of the best, most wonderful experiences of my entire life. And now you're telling me you're not going to ever let me make love to you again. Does that make sense?"

"That's not what I'm telling you," she said.

"You *are* going to let me make love to you again?" I said.

"Sure."

"When?" I said huskily.

"Not tonight."

"When?"

"After a while. After a few more dates."

"How many dates?" I said.

"I don't know yet."

"I see," I said. "And what if I don't go along with that?"

"Then you don't have to see me any more," she said.

"I see," I said.

You will not be altogether thrilled with me when

I tell you that for the next few dates we did things her way. We didn't go to dinner parties or other things that grownups do and we didn't go to restaurants any more because they made her feel uncomfortable. Instead we double-dated with other teenaged couples and we went to a number of teenaged parties where we sat around and listened to loud rock music and smoked pot and didn't talk.

At one such teenaged party, in the sparsely furnished East Village apartment of one of Shelley's friends, I found I could endure the silence no longer. I turned to a boy of about seventeen or so who was sitting next to me and attempted to engage him in conversation.

"Hi," I said.

"Hi," he said.

"My name is Dan," I said.

"I know," he said.

"Oh," I said. Then, because the silence was beginning to close in on me again, I said: "What do you do?"

"What do I what?"

"Do," I said.

"What do you mean?"

"I mean, do you work or go to school or what?"

"Well, you know," he said. "I mean, I used to go to school. But then I like stopped."

"How come?"

"Well, you know. It was too heavy, you know?"

"School was too heavy?" I said.

"Yeah. School, the teachers, whatever was going down. It was too heavy for me, you know? Too heavy a scene. I mean, like there was just no way, you know?"

"So you just dropped out," I said.

He nodded.

"And you're not doing anything at all now?" I said.

He shook his head.

"Well," I said, "if you dropped out of high school, I guess you won't be able to get into college so easily."

"Why do I need to go to college?" he said.

"Well, I don't know," I said, feeling older and squarer every second. "To get a better job, I guess."

"Why do I need a better job?" he said.

"I don't know," I said. "To . . . to be able to buy nice things, to be able to save toward a time when you can . . . enjoy the fruits of your labor and relax and . . . take it easy. . . ."

"I'm taking it easy right now," he said.

I thought about that for a moment and then I nodded my head. "Yeah, I guess you have a point there," I said.

I figured I might be better off taking her to parties with friends my age after all. But my first attempt at this proved disastrous. The men crowded around and slobbered over her just as I had done when I first met her myself, the women patronized, resented and ultimately ignored her, and nobody could quite manage to maintain a conversation with her.

We left early and I took her back to my apartment—only to neck, not to fuck, I assured her. But once in my lair and once we were necking, the crafty old pervert did not permit his hand to be stopped at the boot tops. The more Shelley resisted the hotter I got to be inside of her. We rolled onto the floor and struggled in silence for an incredibly long time, as the absurdity of what I was doing kept washing over me.

Because what I was doing was raping a girl I'd already had sex with, a girl I was (God forbid) going steady with, a girl I had so little in common with that we couldn't carry on an intelligent conversation—and the strangest thing of all was that never before had I dared to physically force myself on anyone in my life.

Eventually, superior strength prevailed, and although I wasn't able to get her into the bedroom or even get her undressed, I did manage to pin her to the floor with one hand and then get the other one inside her clothes to calm her down. Then I thrust my throbbing waga under the crotch of her panties and into her now slippery pussy, and the crime was at last consummated.

Shelley didn't seem at all resentful. She felt she'd tried to stop me, and if she'd failed, she'd failed. Rape is after all not the responsibility of the rapee.

What I finally began to realize about Shelley was that she wasn't even all that crazy about sex. She didn't *dislike* it by any means, and she did of course realize that all her teenaged friends were doing it, but still she wasn't really all that crazy about it. Perhaps, since women are supposed to reach their peak of desire in their late thirties, she simply wasn't old enough. Kittens don't appreciate catnip till they're full grown either.

Shelley and I had about three more dates, one of which included another rape, and then one day she telephoned and sounded somewhat troubled.

"Listen," she said, "like this is really a drag, but I think I'm pregnant."

"*What?*" I said.

"Yeah," she said, "I'm about a month and a half late, and usually I'm pretty regular."

"How could you be pregnant?" I said. "I mean, the pill is supposed to be practically foolproof."

"I don't *use* the pill," she said.

"You don't?" I said.

"No."

"What *do* you use?" I said.

"Nothing," she said.

I had read this before, I knew, in *Goodbye Columbus* or something. And now it was happening to me in real life.

"How could you possibly not *use* anything?" I said.

"Well, like I never thought I *needed* anything," she said.

"But why didn't you at least *tell* me you weren't using anything?" I said.

"I don't know," she said. "I thought it was safe."

I massaged my closed eyeballs with the tips of my fingers, or whatever it is they do at such times in the movies, and then I told her in this sort of tired, resigned voice that I would of course pay for the abortion and that I would make a few phone calls and find out where we had to go in Puerto Rico to have it done.

"Oh wow," she said, "nobody goes to Puerto Rico any more. I mean, like I've got the names of about six doctors in New York alone."

"Okay," I said, "find out how much it'll cost and I'll get the money and go there with you."

At first she said she wouldn't take any money from me because it had been her own fault, but I insisted it was my fault as well and that I could afford it better than she could, so she agreed to let me pay for it. But she didn't want me to come with her—she said she'd feel more comfortable going there with a girl friend. The only thing she wanted was to be able to come back to my apartment afterward and recuperate for a few hours. I said, My God, of course, but why only for a few hours—why not stay all night? I had begun a tender fantasy of nursing my little girl through the long night hours, having the first blue light of dawn find her past the crisis, looking up into my haggard face, her eyes bright with love. Perhaps I'd gather her up in my arms then and ask her to be my wife.

She explained that, wow, she couldn't very well stay the night because what would she tell her mother and everything and that all she wanted to do was come back to my apartment and lie down for a while and, since she'd probably be bleeding all over the place, would it be all right if her girl

friend took care of her and I arranged to be elsewhere?

Sure, I said, anything you say, but I wished there
were more she'd let me do. She said that paying for
it and letting her stay and bleed awhile in my apartment were more than enough. She would call me
later and tell me how much cash she needed and
when I was to be out of the apartment and so on.
I hung up and started in on a fantasy of her dying
in some seedy little tenement in Brooklyn, pitifully
moaning my name as the precious life forces leaked
out of her once perky body, or else hemorrhaging
to death in my very own bed as I watched helpless-
ly in horror and patrol cars outside cut their head-
lights and glided up to encircle the building.

Whenever I get really depressed about something
I call my attorney for advice. When I told him what
I was disturbed about this time he got so nervous
he refused to even discuss it on the telephone. So I
met him on a street corner not far from his office
and we walked along Madison Avenue, pretending
a vast interest in various store window displays,
speaking sotto voce out of the corners of our
mouths, referring to the abortion as "this matter
which has come up," and generally behaving in a
manner that would have aroused the suspicions
of any law enforcement officer a block away.

My attorney's thinking boiled down to two basic
approaches: first, to prepare ourselves now to be
able to prove after Shelley's death that I hadn't
even known her, much less been a party to her
abortion; second, to encourage her to have the

child and to negotiate with her beforehand a favorable contract of child support. I told him he was no goddamned help and he apologized, mumbled good-by and took a circuitous route back to his office.

I called my internist, a strait-laced but kindly gentle man, who offered little hope of having the thing done legally, but who agreed to examine Shelley to make sure she was (a) healthy enough to have an abortion and (b) pregnant enough, and he assured me he would treat her immediately after it had taken place.

Since you have undoubtedly watched endless TV situation comedies involving adults persuading teenagers to do something which was for their own good but which they thought unnecessary, I will spare you the details of how I convinced Shelley to visit my internist. Eventually she did go, was pronounced both healthy and pregnant (I would've given a lot to have seen the look on my gentle doctor's face when the young woman who'd been billed as my fiancée walked into his office in her leather ensemble and her preposterous youth), and a meeting with the abortionist was finally arranged.

I gave Shelley three hundred dollars in small bills, I again vainly tried to talk her into letting me accompany her (I wasn't sure what I dreaded more —going with her or *not* going) and I finally settled back to wait for her in my apartment.

The time passed slowly. The visions of bloody deaths in vacant slum dwellings and of policemen alighting from prowl cars with drawn tommy guns persisted. And then the phone rang.

"Are you all right?" I said.

"Yeah," said Shelley, "but it didn't work."

"What do you mean, it didn't work?"

"Well, the thing that she did just didn't work, that's all, and like I'm supposed to come back in a couple weeks."

"*What* thing didn't work? *What* she?"

"Oh wow," she said. "Well, like it's hard to say now, you know?"

"You mean you're calling from somewhere that you can't speak freely from?"

"Yeah, right," she said.

"But you're sure you're all right?" I said.

"Yeah, I'm positive," she said.

"You want to go and see my internist?"

"*No,*" she said.

"Will you call me as soon as you can talk?"

"Yeah, yeah, I'll try," she said. "But like it might not be for a while. I got a lot of homework to do for school."

When I didn't hear from her the following day I called her again and again she couldn't talk. I asked if she could meet me later that night but she said that she had a big civics test coming up and couldn't leave the house. I told her I might drop by later and see her.

That night I took a cab over to her house. Mrs. Robish answered the door, wearing a rather revealing dressing gown. She looked as though she'd been crying. She seemed pleased to see me and immediately ushered me into the living room and sat me down on the couch.

"Listen, Mrs. Robish," I said, "I know Shelley's studying and everything, but I wonder if you'd mind very much if I took a walk with her for ten or fifteen minutes."

"With Shelley?" she said.

"Yes. Would you mind very much?"

"Shelley isn't here, Mr. Greenburg," she said.

"What?"

"Shelley went out right after supper," she said.

"But she told me she'd be home studying all night tonight," I said. "She has a big civics test tomorrow."

"Maybe she's studying with a friend," said Mrs. Robish.

"But she's not . . . here?" I said.

"No," said Mrs. Robish. "Not."

"Are you sure?" I said.

She smiled. "Mr. Greenburg," she said. "You think perhaps she went out and then sneaked back in and is hiding?"

"No. No, I'm sorry," I said. "It's just that I wanted to talk to her about something important and she said she'd be here, that's all."

"Well," said Mrs. Robish, "it's after ten o'clock. I'm sure she'll be home any minute now. Why don't you wait for her?"

"Well," I said, "I wouldn't want to impose."

"Impose?" she said. "Don't be foolish. Impose." She sniffled and dabbed at her eyes. "Frankly," she said, "I'd welcome the company."

"Is anything wrong, Mrs. Robish?" I said.

"Wrong? What could be wrong?" She sniffled again. "Just because a person's closest friend, a friend to whom she is engaged to marry, does not find her attractive any more, what could possibly be wrong?"

She sank down in a chair next to the couch, took a huge Kleenex out of an enormous box on the coffee table and began to blow her nose. I was afraid she was really going to go into a big crying scene and I didn't know if I could handle it. The tears began to trickle down her cheeks.

"Don't cry, Mrs. Robish," I said. "Please don't."

"Sure, don't cry," she said. "Don't feel sorry for yourself that a wonderful man to whom you have poured out the secrets of a lifetime, a man to whom you've entrusted the intimacies of the heart, a man to whom you've permitted the intimacies of the flesh, a man who has called your bosom one of the three finest bosoms in the entire United States of America—don't be sorry that such a man would throw you away like an old Viva paper towel."

At this point she broke down completely. I rushed over to comfort her, to pat her back, to pat her head, to pat her arm, not knowing what else to pat.

"Please, Mrs. Robish, please. He wasn't worth it," I said.

"Yes, he was," she said through her tears.

"No, he wasn't," I said. "In fact, if you want my

frank opinion, Maurice was a greaseball and a fetishist creep."

She whirled on me. "A *greaseball!*" she said.

"I only meant—"

"After the things he gave me I should sit here and let him be called a *greaseball?*"

"Mrs. Robish, please. I only meant—"

"That man was a *prince* that you're calling a greaseball." She grabbed the hem of her dressing gown. "Look at this. Is this the present of a greaseball?"

"No, listen, I'm sorry I—"

She whipped open her dressing gown to reveal tackily elegant sexy panties, bra, garter belt, stockings and a really voluptuous figure.

"Look at these," she said. "Are these the presents of a greaseball?" She grabbed the lace edge of her bra cup. "Look at the work here. *Look* at it!"

I politely bent to look at it. "Oh yes. Well, that's very—"

"Look at *this.*" She grabbed the lace waist of her panties and held them away from her body to show me. "Look at the work on this and then tell me if it's the present of a greaseball."

"It's really . . . lovely, Mrs. Robish," I stammered, beginning to get turned on in spite of myself.

"You still think he's a greaseball?" she said.

"No. No, I don't. I think he's a . . . a fine human being," I said.

"You do?"

"Yes," I said. "Probably one of the three finest human beings in the entire United States of America."

"Then why"—she choked on a sob—"does he throw me away?"

"I don't know, Mrs. Robish," I said.

"Why does he no longer find me attractive?"

"I don't know."

"Am I suddenly so ugly that no man wants to be seen with me?"

"No, of course not!" I said.

"Am I suddenly so old and flabby that no man wants to make love to me?"

"*No,* Mrs. Robish, not at all!" I said.

She peered down at her figure. "Look at me! Am I at the age of forty-two ready for anything but the garbage can?"

"Oh *yes,* Mrs. Robish—*God,* yes!" I said.

"No, I'm not," she said, breaking down completely. "I'm garbage! Call the Bureau of Sanitation to take me away! Call them! Call them!"

As she gave way to total hysteria I grabbed her and held her and patted her back, in response to which she hugged me so tightly I could scarcely breathe and began showering me with moist grateful kisses.

All at once there was the sound of a key in the lock of the front door. Mrs. Robish and I were blasted apart as if by dynamite. I took a horrified look at the door opening, then at Mrs. Robish's open dressing gown, and made a mad grab to close the latter just as Shelley walked into the apartment.

We stood there in mid-gesture, caught like a freeze frame at the end of a film, as Shelley impassively surveyed the scene.

"You said you'd be home studying for a civics test," I said lamely. "I came by to see you."

"Oh," said Shelley. "Well, I had to go out."

"I see," I said.

"I was studying with some friends," she said.

"I see," I said. I looked at Mrs. Robish. "Do you think it would be all right if I talked with Shelley outside for a minute?" I said.

Mrs. Robish blew her nose and then nodded her head. I led Shelley to the door, looked back at Mrs. Robish and then went outside.

Shelley and I stood awkwardly outside her building.

"I have a confession to make to you," she said.

"What?"

"I wasn't studying at a friend's house just now."

"You weren't?"

"No."

"What were you doing?"

"Scoring some dope."

"I see," I said.

"You mad at me for not being home when I said I'd be?"

"No," I said magnanimously, "not at all."

And then I got a full report on the unsuccessful abortion attempt. It seems that the abortionist, a lady doctor, preferred to use non-surgical means of

181

aborting the fetus if at all possible, and had given Shelley a drug to take which had apparently not worked. I was relieved that surgical procedures were being avoided, and I now envisioned the abortionist as a kindly old Margaret-Sanger-like woman who would protect my little nymphet and unburden her as painlessly as possible of her untimely motherhood.

I called my internist and gave him the name of the drug that Shelley said she'd been given. He said that he was familiar with the drug, that it was reasonably safe, but that so far as he knew it was seldom effective.

Early the following evening I was sitting at my desk, working on a manuscript, when the phone rang. I picked it up and a somewhat nervous accented voice said hello.

"Hi, Mrs. Robish," I said.

"You recognized my voice?"

"You have a very distinctive voice," I said.

"Mr. Greenburg, tell me. You are alone?"

"Alone? Right now, you mean?"

"Right now in your apartment, yes."

"Yes. Why?"

"May I come there and speak with you?"

"Speak to me? I mean, right now?"

"Yes. Unless you don't want me."

"Unless I don't *want* you?"

"I can see that you are busy, Mr. Greenburg," she said.

"Busy? Oh no," I said. "Not at all. If you'd like

to come over, by all means do so. You have the address?"

"Yes, of course I have the address," she said. "How could I come there if I have not the address?"

"Well, good," I said. "When should I expect you then?"

"I leave the house right now," she said.

"Oh, okay, fine. See you in a little while, Mrs. Robish."

I hung up the phone very perplexed. It was entirely possible that she had learned of Shelley's pregnancy and wished to have some dreadful marriage-oriented discussion with me about it. On the other hand, it was just as possible that the intent of her visit was sexual in nature, and, although I wasn't exactly sure how I felt about the prospect of hopping into the sack with Mrs. Robish, I figured I'd keep an open mind on the subject and prepare for such an eventuality should it come to that.

I tore into the bathroom, whipped off my work shirt and jeans and tried on a number of sedate but dressy outfits. At one point I even toyed with the idea of wearing a tie. I finally put the tie away but settled on something far too dressy for at-home wear.

I ran around the apartment, drawing shades and curtains and turning on low, seductive lights. I put a record on the phonograph and then decided it was too contemporary. I changed it to a thing by Wagner. That seemed much too heavy, so I changed it to something hokey and oriental with tinkly bells and drums.

The doorbell rang. I grabbed my tie and put it on after all, changed the record back to Wagner and raced for the door.

"Well, well. Hello there, Mrs. Robish," I said.

She came in, looked interestedly around, took in the romantic lighting, the Wagner record, and then she noticed my hastily tied tie and dress-up clothes.

"Why didn't you tell me you were getting ready to go out?" she said.

"Oh, but I'm not," I said. "I . . . I always dress this way at home when I'm writing. I find it . . . gives the work more dignity this way."

"Ah."

"Well, come in, come in," I said. "Sit down, sit down."

"Thank you, thank you," said Mrs. Robish, "I will, I will." She sat down on the couch.

"What can I get you to drink?" I said.

"Whatever you're having will be fine."

"I suppose you'd like some pear brandy," I said.

"Yes," she said, "do you have any?"

"I'm afraid not," I said.

"Then anything you have will be fine."

I went to the bar and nervously mixed two strong martinis and then returned to the couch. I had a little trouble trying to decide exactly how close to sit to her but finally hit upon a compromise distance and sat down. There was an awkward silence.

"So," I said.

"So," she said.

There was another pause and I noticed she was staring at my hands.

"One of those is for me?" she said finally.

"Oh, of course, of course," I said reddening, and handed her one of the drinks I was holding.

We clinked glasses.

"To whatever . . . it is that would please you the most," I said ambiguously.

"You're very sweet," she said. She reached out to give my neck an affectionate squeeze, which I misconstrued as a pass and immediately started kissing her hand and her wrist and then halfway up her arm before realizing it had merely been a friendly gesture. I withdrew in confusion and tried to compose myself.

"So," said Mrs. Robish again after another silence.

"So," I said.

"Well," she said, "where should I begin?"

"I don't know," I said.

"If you think this is easy for me," she said, "you are mistaken." She looked down at her lap. "Perhaps I should not have come," she said and immediately stood up.

"No, please," I said, restraining her. "I'm *glad* you've come. I'm *delighted* you've come."

"Perhaps you would not be so delighted if you

knew why I am here," she said.

"Oh . . . well . . ."

"Do you know why I am here?"

"Well," I said, "I'm not sure, although I . . . have some suspicions."

"You know," she said, "I was not going to come at first. I said to myself, Pola, why do you have to bother the young man when he probably has enough already on his mind as it is? I said to myself, Pola, leave the young man alone, do not complicate another person's life."

I gazed at her in what I hoped was an intense stare of sympathetic understanding. I leaned in closer to her.

"But then," she said, "I remembered how warm and considerate you were to me the other night at my home . . ."

"Yes . . ." I said softly, leaning closer.

"I remembered all the wonderful sweet things you said to me . . ."

"Yes . . ." I said, leaning even closer.

"I remember how you said to me I was not garbage to be taken away by the Bureau of Sanitation . . ."

"Yes . . ." I said, my lips three inches away from hers.

"I remember how you said I was not so old and flabby and ugly that no man would want to make love to me . . ."

"Yes . . ." I whispered, two inches away.

"And I said to myself, Pola, just because Maurice the Ingrate, Maurice the Pervert, Maurice the

Greaseball wants to throw you into the garbage can and have you taken away by the Bureau of Sanitation does not mean that Mr. Greenburg, the fine young friend of your daughter Shelley, will want this also."

"Yes . . ." I whispered, an inch away.

"I said, If Maurice cannot give you what you want, then you will ask the handsome Mr. Greenburg and perhaps he will not refuse you. I said, Perhaps he will be able to give you what you require or at least not be disgusted by the request."

"Anything," I breathed, practically touching her lips, "anything at all . . . just ask it."

She cupped my face and gazed deeply into my eyes. "Can you lend me four hundred dollars?" she said.

I knew that she had not actually said what I thought she had said, but it seemed best to check. "Can I do what?" I whispered.

"Lend me four hundred dollars?"

Overcome with sudden weariness, I collapsed back against the cushions of the couch.

"I *knew* I should not have asked it," she said. "I knew it. I said to myself, Pola, don't ask him. Don't. It is not fair for you to burden another with your problems. It is not fair for you to ask another person with problems of his own for such a sum of money, even if he has it and could spare it and if you yourself need it so desperately since you lost your job that you and your daughter will have to live on dry cereal and week-old bread and spoiled milk for the rest of your lives."

187

She began to cry. "I said, Don't ask it of him even though it would be only for a short period of time and you would cheerfully pay him twelve and a half per cent interest on the loan and as collateral put up your dishes, your vacuum cleaner and your clothes," she said. "I said, Better you should get the money elsewhere, from strangers. I said, Better you should sell your body in Times Square to sailors and perverts and give half of what you earn to a pimp and contract a social disease than to embarrass such a wonderful, warm and well-to-do young man as Mr. Greenburg. I said——"

"No! Please! Stop!" I said. I couldn't take it any more. I ran to my desk, grabbed my wallet, ran back to the couch and dumped a bunch of five- and ten-dollar bills into her lap. "Here! Take it!" I said. "Here! Please!"

I ran and got my checkbook and whipped off a check for the remaining amount and thrust it into her hands. "Here! Here's the money! Take it! Please!"

Terribly moved, she looked at the bills in her lap and at the check. Then she looked up at me. Then she handed them all back.

"I can't," she said. "I can't take the money. Here. Please. Take it back."

"No, you take it," I said. "Please. Take it. I want you to take it. Please. Do me a favor and take it. Please."

I pushed it all back at her. She pushed it all back at me. It shuttled back and forth between us for several seconds, finally ending up back in my hands. She looked up at me with overpowering emotion.

"You are the finest human being I have ever met," she said, and kissed me full on the mouth.

I melted. She hugged me tight, kissed me again, then, holding me by the shoulders at arm's length, she looked at me and smiled.

"All right," she said. She shook her head and sighed. "All right." She sighed again. "I'll take the money." She took the money out of my hands and stood up. "God bless you," she said, her eyes wet, "God bless you."

She went to the door. "God bless you," she said again. She opened the door, blew me a kiss and softly closed the door behind her.

Ten or twelve days after that Shelley again visited the little old abortionist and was given the same drug, and with the same result. She was told to appear once more in a week or so for a third attempt. Time was running out. Shelley was by now two and a half months' pregnant, and I knew it was extraordinarily unsafe to have an illegal abortion after the third month of pregnancy.

The third administration of the drug proved unsuccessful as well, and the doctor told Shelley she would now attempt another abortive technique, more severe than the previous one but also non-surgical. The doctor warned there might be unpleasant after-effects, and so I was able to persuade Shelley to return to my apartment after the treatment and spend the night in my care. She agreed, worked out an elaborate lie to tell her mother, and told me to expect her about 10 P.M.

Ten P.M. came and went without Shelley's arrival, but I knew how difficult it was to predict what time one would be home from even a *legitimate* doctor's appointment, and so I didn't become really worried until about midnight. From midnight to one o'clock I found myself doing a lot of nervous humming and pacing and twitching, and from one o'clock to two o'clock I was involved in a heated discussion with God about taking me too literally when I'd said He could do anything if He would just let me screw her. At two-thirty the doorbell rang and when I saw it was Shelley I grabbed her and held her so tightly I almost strangled her.

"My God," I said, leading her over to a chair, "how do you feel?"

"Oh wow," she said, "a little tired."

"I can just imagine," I said. "You poor kid. Are you all right?"

"I guess so," she said, slumping into a half-slouch in the chair.

"What took so long?" I said. "Were there complications or what?"

"Oh no, no complications," she said.

"Then what took so long?"

"Well, like on the way back from the abortionist we ran into some kids we knew who were going to this new discotheque in the East Village and it sounded like a groove, so we went with them."

I massaged my closed eyelids with the tips of my fingers. "Let me see if I've got this straight," I said carefully. "After your abortion you went *dancing?* Is that what you're telling me?"

"Yeah, but only for a couple hours," she said.

"I see," I said, trying mightily to remain composed.

"What's wrong with *you?*" she said.

"Well, aside from the fact that while you were dancing all of your guts could have slid out of your crotch onto the dance floor, you happen to be about four and a half hours late and I was a little concerned about your safety."

She gave me a look of unbelievable disappointment and sadly shook her head. "Oh wow," she said. "Oh wow."

Then she went to bed.

Our relationship, if that's what you want to call it, was not wonderful after that. The fourth abortion attempt had failed and a fifth one was arranged for the following weekend, when I would be in Chicago on business and Shelley and her girlfriend could use my apartment.

I had by that point caught Shelley in a number of pointless untruths, such as: (1) the "girl friend" who accompanied her on her several trips to the abortionist was sometimes a real girl friend named Cathy and sometimes a former boy friend named Peter, for whom, she insisted, she no longer felt anything but "friendship"; (2) two occasions on which she'd broken dates with me to be with her lonely widowed mother had actually been spent with her lonely widowed mother and Peter; (3)

the kindly white-haired lady doctor who was trying to abort Shelley was neither kindly nor white-haired nor was she a doctor—she was a tough Puerto Rican woman who'd merely assisted another abortionist long enough to learn the trade and go into business herself, and the technique she was currently using on Shelley involved filling her crotch with a hideous concoction of penicillin and molten Lifebuoy soap.

I had partially suspected the first two things, and had no idea at all of the third. But the confrontation during which all of this came out took place in my bedroom as Shelley watched me get ready to leave for the airport and a plane I barely had time to catch, and so there was little chance to do more than shudder and close the suitcase and walk to the door. I made Shelley promise to call my internist at the slightest sign of trouble and I made her promise to keep the front door double-locked at all times, to not let anyone but her girl friend Cathy into the apartment, to not use anything stronger than pot, and I hadn't the slightest hope that she was even listening to me.

As I opened the door to leave, Shelley said, "Hey," and grabbed me and hugged me. "I'm sorry I told you all those things that weren't true," she said into my shoulder.

"That's all right," I said.

"You don't like me any more, do you?" she said.

"Sure I do. Sure I like you, Shelley," I said.

"No, you don't," she said. "I can tell. I lied to you a lot, and I don't know why I did, because it was so stupid, but I just did. And now you don't trust me any more and I don't blame you. But it's really sad, because the thing of it is . . . I love you."

With that she started to cry for the first time since I'd met her. I had never expected her to say anything about loving me—I hadn't spoken much about love to anyone at that point in my life—and it really rocked me. I held her and I told her how much she meant to me, because suddenly she did mean a great deal to me, and I told her that I guessed I probably loved her too and that I would call her from Chicago and to take care. Then I walked out the door and ran out onto the street to hail a taxi.

I suppose I should have stayed. I suppose I should have canceled the flight reservation and called off the business trip and stayed with the poor little pregnant girl in my apartment who'd just blurted out that she loved me. But that is really more what they do in the movies than what you do in real life. In real life you don't call off the business trip and you don't cancel the flight reservation, you hail the taxi and get on the plane, no matter how strong your premonitions of disaster. In real life you don't even get off an airplane that is still on the ground though you've just been hit with not the premonition but the *certainty* that the plane will explode in mid-air somewhere over New Jersey, because you would rather face certain death and dismemberment than the possibility of the public ridicule you might have to endure while demanding that they open the big door again and let you off the aircraft.

I telephoned Shelley from my parents' home in Chicago and she informed me that the fifth attempt at abortion had proven unsuccessful as well but that she was feeling fine. I made her promise to visit my internist anyway and I said that we would get the whole thing resolved once and for all when I got back to New York (she was now in her third month of pregnancy, so we *had* to get it resolved once and for all when I got back to New York), and then I told her I loved her and I'd be home soon, and I hung up the phone.

My parents, though forbidden by me for many years to inquire about my plans for marriage, were trying so hard to keep from asking me anything about the girl I had just spoken to and said "I love you" to that they were in almost physical pain.

When I got back to New York I immediately began making phone calls and arrangements for taking Shelley to Puerto Rico for a surgical abortion under sterile and semilegal conditions. Shelley wasn't at all enthusiastic about the idea, but she appeared to accept my tone of authority.

My apartment seemed much as I had left it, and if any drug parties or orgies had taken place there in my absence, no evidence of either remained. Just as an afterthought, however, I checked my desk and the small night table by the side of my bed to make sure my valuables were still intact. I felt sort of sheepish about doing it, but I did it anyway.

The small supply of cash I keep there appeared to be just as I'd left it, my two 35mm. cameras were still there, and I was just about to concede that my inclination to check my valuables had been paranoid when it occurred to me that my tiny Minox camera was missing.

I couldn't believe it. And yet it wasn't there. I emptied out the drawers of the night table and picked through the contents. No Minox. I emptied out the drawers of my desk and went through them in painstaking detail. I systematically tore the entire apartment apart, but nowhere could I find my Minox camera. I telephoned Shelley and told her.

"Are you sure you looked everywhere?" she said.

"I'm positive," I said. "Honey, do you have any idea where it could be?"

"I don't even know what a Minox camera *looks* like," she said, and I believed her.

"You don't think that Cathy could have taken it for any reason, do you?" I said. "Not to steal it, I mean, just to borrow it for some purpose?"

"Why would Cathy do a thing like that?" she said.

"I don't know," I said. "Listen, Shelley, do you swear to me that nobody but you and Cathy was in my apartment while I was gone?"

"Oh wow," she said, "what do you think we did—invite all our friends over and shoot dope?"

"No, don't be silly," I said, though of *course*

that's what I thought. "Just swear to me that no-body but you and Cathy was here while I was gone and I'll believe you. Okay?"

"Oh wow," said Shelley.

"Do you swear?" I said.

There was a long silence at the other end of the line. Then: "If I tell you something will you be mad at me?"

"What?" I said wearily.

"Well, on Saturday a couple of kids I know dropped by your place and wanted to come in . . ."

"Yes . . . ?"

"Well, I told them I'd like promised not to let anyone in but Cathy and everything . . ."

"Yes . . . ?"

"Well, so like one of them had to go to the *bathroom* and everything . . ."

"Yes . . . ?"

"Well, wow. I mean, like I couldn't tell them not to use the *bathroom,* now could I?"

"And after they used the bathroom, did they leave then?"

"Well, sort of. Yeah."

"Did they leave after using the bathroom or didn't they?"

"Well, like not that very *second,* no. But they didn't stay too long after that."

"Shelley," I said, "the Minox that is missing was in the top drawer of the little night table next to the bed in the bedroom. If you can assure me that you were with your friends every minute they were in my apartment and that they didn't go into the bedroom, then I am willing to drop this whole discussion right now. Are you willing to give me that assurance?"

"Oh wow."

"Are you?"

"Well, I was with them *most* of the time. I mean, I wasn't with them when they went into the goddam *bathroom*, for God's sake. . . ."

"Go on. . . ."

"Well, now that I think of it, one of the guys, a kid named Joe, might possibly have wandered downstairs into your bedroom for a second or so, just to look around, like. But he came out right away, I know that, and besides, he wouldn't have taken your Minox. I can guarantee you that."

"What makes you so sure?"

"Because. He doesn't do that kind of stuff. Not any more, I mean. I mean, not since he's been back."

"He doesn't do *what* stuff any more since he's been back from *where?*"

There was a long sigh at the other end of the line. "I know you're going to get the wrong idea about this," she said.

"Tell me anyway," I said.

"Well, Joe just got out of jail for stealing cars. But like that's all the more reason why he wouldn't have stolen your Minox, because he'd be afraid of violating his parole. See?"

Now it was *my* turn to be silent. It was clear to me that the further I probed into this the worse things I would find, but it was too late to stop.

"Shelley," I said in this very controlled voice, "you gave me your word before I left that you wouldn't let anyone but Cathy into my apartment, and when I came back you swore to me that you had kept your promise. And now you've admitted to me that you permitted a man who is on parole for grand larceny into my bedroom, and still you insist he is not responsible for my missing Minox. Now does that sound reasonable to you, or do you think I have legitimate grounds for being suspicious?"

"Oh wow," she said. "Okay. Look. I knew Joe went into your bedroom. But I know he didn't take your Minox, because I saw him go through the drawers in your night table and I know that all he took was odds and ends."

At some point I was going to have to just stop asking questions, I really was. "What sort of . . . odds and ends did this convicted felon friend of yours take out of my night table drawers?" I said.

"Just some Chapsticks and some . . . waddaya-callems."

"What *kind* of waddayacallems?"

"Cundrums, I think, is what you call them."

"You mean condoms?" I said. I had once bought a package of very expensive premoistened condoms but had never used them.

"Yeah, cundrums. That and the Chapsticks was all he took, I swear. I told him to not even take that, but he did. He was a little stoned and he was like goofing on the stuff in your drawers, but even though he was playing around with the Minox, he didn't take it. I would have seen it if he had."

"I'm sure you would have," I said. "All right, Shelley, here is what you are going to do. You are going to call your friend Joe the convicted felon and you are going to tell him I know all about the condoms and the Chapsticks and the Minox. You are going to tell him he can keep the condoms and he can keep the Chapsticks, but you are going to tell him that unless he has my Minox back here in my apartment within twenty-four hours I am going straight to the police and he is going straight back to jail."

There was a lot of heavy breathing at the other end of the line.

"Will you tell him that?" I said.

"I'll tell him," she said and hung up.

I was so furious I was shaking. I could just imagine the scene in my apartment while I was gone—the drug-taking, the amused "goofing" on the contents of my drawers—and I felt terribly violated and betrayed.

Obviously, the only true thing she had ever told me was that she was pregnant—and I wouldn't even be sure of that if my own internist hadn't verified it. *But pregnant by whom?* Joe, the stoned felon? Peter, the former lover and alleged present "friend"? Cliff, the cocky entrepreneur who'd allegedly never made it into bed with her? Or perhaps she was pregnant by one of her many lovers I didn't even know by name and who couldn't afford to pay for an abortion as I could. To think that I'd believed her when she said she loved me! Bitch!

Well, my little Nabokovian escapade had cost me an expensive miniature camera and seven hundred dollars in cash—three hundred to Shelley and four hundred to her mother—for just three lays. At those prices I could have had a tag team of call girls. It was now definitely over with Shelley, and I didn't much care if they poured penicillin and molten Lifebuoy into her twat till it came out of her nostrils.

Shelley called back to say she had talked to Joe and he'd sworn he never took my Minox, and I could go to the cops if I wanted to, but she believed him. I was barely civil to her.

The next day I filed a claim with my insurance company for the missing Minox. Although I was truly furious, the only report I gave the police about the missing camera was for the insurance claim, and when they asked me if I had any idea who might have stolen it, I said I hadn't. (The Wronged Person Too Noble to Be a Stoolie.)

A couple of days after that Shelley called to say that she didn't know whether I was still interested but she'd gone back to the abortionist and had another treatment, and that this time it had been successful. I asked her if she was all right, and she said she was. I asked her where it had happened and she said in her mother's bathroom. She'd felt it coming, she said, and just gone into the bathroom and aborted it into the toilet. She also said something else which I dismiss as a teenager's overactive imagination, because it's too disturbing to take it seriously. What she said was that she forced herself to look down at the mess in the toilet bowl before she flushed it away, and that it had been a boy.

I never heard from Shelley again, although I did come across some 8 x 10 photographs I'd taken of her once and they made me terribly sad.

About two months after I filed my claim the insurance company sent me a voucher good for another Minox. I picked up the new camera at my local camera store, brought it home and was just about to put it away when I saw it: the missing Minox, lying there in the bottom of my camera bag.

And suddenly I didn't know anything at all about what had really happened between me and my teenaged mistress, because now any of it or all of it, including her loving me, could just as likely have been the truth as not. The only thing I did know for sure was that, whatever the real truth was, it was now too late to matter.

17

At the risk of giving further ammunition to racists and religious bigots and other xenophobes, I'd like to confirm something which they've been saying for years but which you already knew anyway —that all us swarthy little Hebes would like nothing better than to get into the pants of all those tall blonde *shiksas*, just as all black men would like nothing better than to get into those selfsame blonde-bushed white-assed pants, just as all blue-collar workers want to get into the pants of all white-collar workers, all Democrats want to get into the pants of all Republicans, all militant student activists want to get into the pants of all policemen and policewomen, and so on.

What they never told us but what is nonetheless true is that all the blonde-bushed *shiksa* cuties, whether or not they admitted it to their friends or even to themselves, were just as anxious to have us swarthy little Hebes fooling around in there among their thighs as we were to be there ourselves.

Sadly, this knowledge was spared me until such

time as it was no longer very relevant to my scoring capability. Not that I hadn't been to bed with Gentiles or even with blonde Gentiles. It's just that I had never had the pleasure of sleeping with the authentic blonde American Protestant cheerleader promised all of us consumers-in-training in the Coke and Pepsi ads of our youth, and I hadn't even been within range of such a girl until the day I first met Bonnie.

Bonnie was the perfect Pepsi girl, was a sometime model who had in fact been in an ad for one cola or another, though not necessarily Pepsi, and who had indeed been a cheerleader in *both* high school and college. She was tall and long-legged, she had nice little breasts and perfect white teeth and shoulder-length blonde hair with a little flip at the ends which swung back and forth in slow motion just like the mousy-to-marvelous commercial whenever she shook her head. You knew her underwear was always clean.

Bonnie when I met her had no real boy friend. She lived with three other girls in an apartment in the East Eighties and there were always a couple of tall, big-boned, shambling guys with horn-rimmed glasses and white socks hanging around the place waiting for one of the girls to get ready and go somewhere. I wasn't big-boned and I didn't wear white socks, but I did wear horn-rimmed glasses at the time and I did tend to shamble, and so I never figured it was too peculiar that a girl as pretty as Bonnie was going out with me until I actually got her outside the apartment, and then I always became so self-conscious I could never do much more with her than talk.

Bonnie was shy, but she was a pretty good talker once you drew her out, and she had a pretty good sense of humor too, so we enjoyed each other's company. She was very virginal and soapy-smelling and proper, so I never actually tried anything sexual with her for fear of offending her, and our good-night kisses at her door were chaste and uniformly closed-mouthed.

After I'd been taking her out for about two months I decided one night to bring her back to my apartment and introduce the subject of sex at least verbally to see what kind of reaction I might get. The reaction I got, as you may have guessed, was that during the two months she'd been going out with me she'd also been going out with one of the tall, big-boned shambling guys who hung around the apartment she lived in, she'd been sleeping with him for the past three weeks, and now she was running off with him to somewhere in Utah to get married.

I was in a state of shock for about a week. The idea that someone who was not only no betterlooking than I but who wore white socks had been getting into those sweet *shiksa* panties while I had been settling for chaste little lip-presses at the doorjamb every Saturday night made me crazy. I spent several days under the delusion that I had been in love with her without daring to acknowledge it, sure that if I had made my move before the guy in the white socks it would be *me* she was running off to Utah to marry and not him.

By the end of the week I had snapped out of this bizarre (though probably not incorrect) notion and I made myself a solemn promise: never again would I play it slow with any girl. From here on in it was going to be full court press from the starting buzzer of the very first date with every girl I went out with. (Remarkable how many sports-oriented metaphors I use, considering I'm such an avowed non-athlete, wouldn't you say?)

Shortly after taking this vow I went to a party and met a girl who looked a little like Bonnie, and I selected her as my next target.

Her name was Lizabeth. She was just as blonde as Bonnie and just as Protestant, and she was almost as good-looking, and I was obsessed with pronging her as soon as possible to make up for the great stupidity with Bonnie.

Lizabeth had done some modeling for *Vogue*, and in her conversations she mixed literary pretensions with name-dropping anecdotes and cutesy fashion-mag expressions. She was a wood sprite, but one made of solid wood. She spoke in a husky, provocative voice that produced instant crotch thoughts in my mind.

For our first date I suggested a private picnic in my leafy, green-lit back-yard garden with a picnic basket packed by one of New York's suaver French restaurants. Lizabeth was incredibly impressed. Af-

206

ter clearing the checkered tablecloth of chicken bones and croissant crumbs, I pulled her down next to me in the grass. We lay in each other's arms under a starry, fire-escape-framed sky, and I began slowly kissing and fondling and squeezing her, to the accompaniment of her cutesy impersonal endearments and her fashionable little cries of rapture.

I hadn't really gotten any further than general necking when I thoughtlessly stuck my tongue into her ear, which produced immediate writhing and moaning and a husky explanation that this was the Big Button with her and she wasn't yet ready to have it pushed. I agreed to this aural detour, but by lots of sneaky maneuvering I had by the end of the evening progressed to hand-on-the-buttocks-inside-the-panties, at which point I was again stopped and brought down hard on the three-yard line as the final gun went off. As we stood up to straighten our clothes and prepare for taking her back home I had every expectation that when the game was resumed on our next date I would carry the ball quickly over the goal line on the very first play.

My next date with Lizabeth was unfortunately a late one, with other people present, and I had to be content with hurried kisses and tongues-in-cheeks at her door. Our third date proved to be equally unproductive owing to some mysterious female ailment, darkly hinted at but never named, which was probably nothing more exotic than menstruation. However, assurances were given by means of winks and squeezes that next time would be different.

Next time *was* different, but only in that the mysterious ailment had been displaced upward to her chest, causing a lot of bronchial congestion and precluding even the exploration of mouths because of sudden grave concern for my health. To mollify my growing feelings of frustration, an elliptical invitation to spend a weekend together in the country was wheezed out of Lizabeth's tortured lungs, and I got through the next week with visions of long blonde hair beside mine on the pillowcase.

Well, the carnal weekend in the country somehow never quite materialized, even though AAA road maps were spread out on floors and miracle-marked in crimson ink. And so I trotted gamely after the dangling carrot of crotch which was always just a little bit ahead of me, as the leaves in my garden turned yellow, fell to the ground, blew crunchy brown against my patio door and eventually disappeared beneath a soot-dusted blanket of snow.

It was not quite as simple as Lizabeth's being a deliberate tease, I felt sure of that. But I was ready to concede that it might have been more than plain bad luck that was keeping me outside of Lizabeth's loins. I was not yet willing to drop her, since the very next date might well be The One, and I was even more unwilling after getting out pencil and paper and checking my dating lists and calculating that Lizabeth at that point represented an investment of some three hundred and fifty hours and some eleven hundred or so dollars.

Any stockbroker will tell you that if a stock isn't doing anything you should sell it, no matter how much you've invested in it and no matter how much lower it is now than when you bought it. I have always recognized the soundness of such advice and have never been able to take it, which explains why I have never done well in the stock market and why I continued to pour even more dollars and hours into my investment in Lizabeth.

One night late in February as we lay in front of the crackling fire in Lizabeth's pretentiously quaint and fashion-mag-cutesy one-room apartment, I again started work on her and before either of us realized it I'd progressed straight through hand-on-the-sweater to palm-on-the-belly to fingers-in-the-actual-bush. With the gesture of someone who has just discovered a rather long and unfamiliar human hair in their bowl of vichyssoise, Lizabeth plucked my hand out of her pants and dropped it neatly to the floor. And in that instant I saw with almost blinding clarity what had been crouching just below the level of consciousness since our very first date together: she who makes rapturous little cries at tongue-in-the-ear but who remains completely unmoved by fingers-in-the-bush or hand-on-the-buttocks-inside-the-panties is not likely to ever use her privates for anything more exhilarating than making peepee.

And so, smiling the smile of one who may be

leaving behind him a monetary and temporal investment sufficient to outfit and train the San Diego Chargers for an entire season, but who knows that there is nothing ahead of him but a long frozen football field stretching away into infinity with no goalposts at the end of it, I drew on my sheepskin coat and stepped out into the winter night.

18

By a fantastic coincidence, the week I realized the truth about Lizabeth was the week that old Bonnie came back to town. She wasn't married after all, having chickened out at the last minute and left behind an amazed, white-socked and even more shambling ex-fiancé.

She seemed no less virginal than before, but I now had to compensate not only for my previous stupidity with Bonnie but for my even greater stupidity with Lizabeth, and so her apparent virginity no longer deterred me in the least.

I took her out to dinner, poured lots of alcohol down her throat, brought her back to my apartment and leapt upon her almost before the door was closed. She permitted the kissing and the fondling but she was not game for anything else, what with having recently been through the traumatic and guilt-filled near marriage, and what with the hour being so late and her having to be at work so early the following morning.

But I had been too long denied. Hardened by months spent on the brink of Lizabeth's brink, I kept up the kissing, the fondling, the snappy patter and the fancy footwork until Bonnie's eyelids clanged shut and she pleaded to be taken home.

Thinking fast, I pointed out that her office was far closer to my apartment than it was to hers, and if she simply stayed overnight she could save herself considerable traveling both now and in the morning, and spend the time she saved asleep. I assured her there would be no love-making unless she herself requested it (I wondered if my voice was being piped out into the streets), and if she didn't trust me she could have the king-sized bed to herself and I would sleep on the couch.

She groggily said she couldn't very well sleep over since, among other things, she didn't even have a toothbrush with her. But I, well-prepared little devil that I am, whipped out two toothbrushes, one yellow and one blue, each hygienically sealed in plastic. I asked her which color she preferred (an old salesman's trick known as "closing on a minor point"), and she said the blue one—thus inadvertently settling the larger issue by deciding the smaller one. I broke the seal and handed her the blue toothbrush. Too sleepy to backtrack at this point, she shrugged and sighed and trudged off to brush her teeth and wash up for bed.

In the forty or fifty seconds it took her in the bathroom, I stripped down to my Fruit-of-the-Looms, snapped off the lights and dove into bed. Bonnie opened the bathroom door and peered into darkness.

212

"Hey," she said, "what happened to all the lights out there?"

"Well," I said, "I got tired of waiting for you so I just got into bed."

"Uh, weren't you going to sleep on the couch or something?" she said.

"No, not exactly. What I said was if you didn't *trust* me I would sleep on the couch."

"Oh. Well, perhaps it would be better if you did that. If you don't mind too much, I mean."

"Mind? Of course not. I'll just get up now and try to find some extra sheets and blankets and then I'll make up the narrow, uncomfortable old couch and go to sleep on it."

"Is it really that uncomfortable?" she said.

"Yes, but I don't mind. If you're at all uneasy about sleeping in the same bed with me and feel I might rape you or something, I'll be perfectly happy to sleep there."

"Oh hell," she said. "I guess a king-sized bed is big enough for both of us. Just promise me you won't try anything, because I really am exhausted and I really do have to get up awfully early for work."

"Not only will there be no love-making unless you verbally *request* it," I said, "but you will have to beg me to even kiss you good night."

"Good," she said. "Now what is there for me to sleep in?"

"Well, I don't have any pajamas or anything, but I do have an old sweat suit if you'd care to use

213

that. Of course I don't know for sure that it's been laundered since I wore it to take judo lessons in at the Y, so it might be a *little* gamey . . ."

She sighed and said never mind and closed the bathroom door. Before coming out again she turned off the bathroom light, but my eyes were already accustomed to the dark and so I could see quite clearly what she'd chosen to sleep in: her panties and her half slip pulled up over her breasts. I wanted to jump her immediately, but I remembered my promise and decided to bide my time. She groped her way to the bed in the dark and climbed underneath the covers.

"Well, good night," she said. "Set the alarm for seven-thirty, please. And remember your promise."

"Good night," I said, setting the clock radio in the headboard. "And don't worry about my promise, because as I said before, if you want even a good-night kiss you'll have to beg for it."

She giggled. "Okay," she said, "may I please have a good-night kiss?"

"That's not begging," I said.

"Please, please, *please,* may I have a good-night kiss?"

"Well, all right," I said, "but only one."

I found her in the bed and kissed her good night, the sensation of our two largely undressed bodies together under the covers very odd and new and nice. It was a lovely kiss and she permitted it to continue awhile, with attendant hugs and caresses. When I sensed she was about ready to pull away I did so first, and made a big thing out of turning my back and arranging myself for sleep at the opposite side of the bed.

"Okay," I said, "that's all you get."

"Okay," she said.

"Good night," I said.

"Good night," she said.

I fluffed up my pillow and tried to relax. Lying next to me under the covers in her slip and panties was the best-looking girl I had ever met—a gorgeous, soapy-smelling, blonde, Protestant former cheerleader—and it seemed obvious that unless I did something churlish and soon and broke my promise, she was going right to sleep. And at seven-thirty the next morning she would get up and out of my bed and into her clothes and out of my apartment, and although she would probably respect the hell out of me for keeping my word, I might never again be so close to scoring with her.

"Pssst! Hey, Bonnie," I whispered, "you still awake?"

"What is it?" she said.

"Well, nothing, except I can't seem to get to sleep."

"How do you know?" she said. "We haven't even been in bed for more than five minutes."

"I know, but I can tell I'm not going to be able to sleep. I'm very edgy."

"What are you edgy about?"

"I don't know, but I've found that when I'm unusually edgy it helps sometimes if someone holds me for a while."

"I thought there wasn't going to *be* any of this," she said. "I thought you were going to let me go to *sleep.*"

"Of course I am, of course. And I promised you I wouldn't make love to you unless you asked me to, and I meant it. But I had no idea I'd be feeling this edgy, and I just thought that if you wouldn't mind holding me for just a few minutes, then I could relax and it would help me get to sleep. If you'd rather not, though, just say so and I'll understand. I'll just stay up all night and be edgy."

A pause. A sigh. Then: "Okay, come here and I'll hold you. But just for a little while, and then you've really got to let me get some sleep."

I snuggled over to her and she put her arms around me and we made ourselves comfortable under the covers. It was wonderful.

"You don't mind cuddling like this, do you?" I said.

"Oh no," she said. "In fact it's really very sweet."

"Good," I said. "I'm feeling a lot less edgy already."

I shifted slightly in her arms and scrunched down lower in the bed.

"Hey," she said, "what are you doing?"

"Who, me?"

"Yes, you."

"Nothing."

"If you're doing nothing, then where is your head?"

"Oh, is *that* what's bothering you? That my head is on your breasts?"

216

"Yes."

"What's the matter, don't you have any maternal instincts?"

"Yes, but you're flattening them out."

"Don't worry, they'll go right back when you stand up. I'll fluff them up a little and they'll go right back."

"I don't think this is such a good idea, I really don't."

"You don't want my head on your breasts?"

"No."

"Okay," I said and scrunched down a little lower and laid my cheek against her belly.

"Hey," she said nervously, "come on now."

"What do you mean, 'come on now'? You said you didn't want my head on your breasts, and so I moved it."

"You said you weren't going to pull any funny stuff. That's what you said, remember?"

"That's not what I said at all. What I said was that if there was going to be any love-making, any actual intercourse, you would have to ask me. That's all I said. I didn't say a thing about where I was going to put my head. I don't even see what you're so excited about anyway. I'm just resting my head on your belly, that's all. I'm not even touching you with my hands. See?" I held up my hands. "Here are my hands. I'll keep them behind my back. Okay? How's that?"

"I don't think you're being very fair," she said, and for the first time I detected the vaguest trace of ambivalence in her voice.

The clock was running out on me. It was now or never. I inched my face a little lower and pressed my ample chin into her panty-covered *mons veneris*.

"Don't do that," she said, but rather unconvincingly.

"Okay," I said, "I'll stop in just a second."

I thrust my chin into her mound of Venus again and released the pressure, and thrust again.

"Don't do that," she said, but now she was whispering.

I continued rhythmically diddling her through her panties with my chin until her hips began moving responsively under my head. And when I reached up and grabbed the cheeks of her sweet tushy and pulled her panties down, she placed her hands on my head and, with a little whimper of resignation, she pressed my face into her bush.

Above me, very far away, I heard her crying something in this weeny weeny little voice, and eventually I realized that what she was crying was "No no no no no no no . . ."

I stopped a moment and whispered: "Are you all right?"

"Don't pay any attention to me," she said, quickly pressing my face back to where it had been, "that's just a noise I make."

And then the strangest transformation took place: gone forever was the virginal little pompom girl, and in her place appeared a mature, fully operational, sexual woman. I went back to my job, giddy with sneaky success, working her over so thoroughly with my tongue that she was soon whipping her head back and forth, and before long the weeny weeny little "no's" changed to somewhat deeper "nows."

I stopped licking the clitoris and called softly up to the head: "Do you want me to make love to you?"

"Yes," she whispered.

"Are you sure?" I said.

"Yes," she said, "*please,* yes."

"Then ask me."

"Oh, God," she said, grabbing me under the arms and pulling me up on top of her, "fuck me, please, fuck me—my God, please *fuck me!*"

And so I did. I fucked her eyes out. I had never been so good in bed before and I shall never be so good in bed again. I fucked her lying down, I fucked her standing up, I fucked her on her side, I fucked her sitting up, and standing on her head, and while carrying her around the room. I fucked her in every position I'd ever learned in *Love without Fear* and in about forty new ones I made up on the spot. I fucked her for all the nights I'd only been granted chaste good-night kisses at her door and I fucked her for running off with the white-socked wonder and I fucked her for reminding me of my promise not to fuck her unless she asked me to. I fucked her for all the swarthy little Hebes who had never and who would never fuck a beautiful blonde *shiksa* and finally I fucked her because I knew this was the best night of fucking I would ever have in my entire life.

I was stretched out on top of her, finally spent, as the clock radio turned itself on and we realized that it was seven-thirty and we hadn't slept a second.

"Wake up," I said. "It's time for work."

The peppiness of this remark was wasted on Bonnie. She got up wearily and went into the bathroom to wash, leaving behind her in bed all the affection of the past several hours. I followed her into the bathroom.

"Hey," I said, "what's the matter?"

She shook her head. I didn't ask her again because I knew. Not only had I kept her awake all night and presented her with the necessity of working a full groggy day without benefit of sleep, but I had tricked her into something she deeply resented, and I don't just mean dropping her drawers. I'd tricked her into dropping her virginal little-girl mask, into forcing her to acknowledge her own womanliness and her own sexuality and her own grownupness. I mean, here was an adult female who was having fairly regular sex with adult males and she was still signing her letters with little smiling faces. It was as if I had been her first lover.

I watched her get dressed and made up and I was fascinated, not only because she was a beautiful woman and it is fascinating to watch one of those anyway, but because I realized that each successive article of clothing or make-up that she put on was another layer of something that insulated her from the intimacy of the hours we'd spent together in bed. By the time she was ready to leave the apartment she was so detached and so grumpy, all she would grant me in the way of a good-by kiss was a little peck on the cheek.

I didn't care really. I had what I wanted, at least for the moment. I had scored, and it was the best score I had ever made. Usually when I miss even a few hours of sleep at night I'm a total wreck the following day. But now I was so giddy and flushed with triumph I fairly galloped through the next sixteen hours.

I telephoned Bonnie at her job just to say hello and to tell her she was terrific and I missed her. I asked her to have dinner with me that night. She said she didn't know. She was very tired and perhaps what she really needed was to go home after work and go right to sleep. We made a date for the following night, but I was pretty pissed off. I wanted to see her again and I didn't want to wait till the following night.

I called up a lady I knew (a platonic friend, as a matter of fact) and asked whether she'd like to have dinner with me that evening. The lady said okay. I went over to her house for cocktails, and I was still in such a madman state that before I'd been there for ten minutes I'd planted my mouth on hers and run my hand up her leg, and the lady couldn't believe it. We went to bed and screwed and never even got to the restaurant at all. I figured it served Bonnie right.

The next day I called Bonnie at work to tell her

what time I'd pick her up for dinner, and she seemed very evasive. She said she was still tired and couldn't we make it another night? I was angry and said no. I said I wanted to see her tonight. She said she would agree to see me if I insisted, but I would have to promise to get her home early, and if we went to bed I would *still* have to promise to get her home early.

I told her to take a change of clothes with her and spend the night at my place. She said she couldn't do that. I said why? She said because. She couldn't decide now what she was going to feel like wearing when she woke up tomorrow morning. I asked her whether she wanted me to decide for her. What did I mean? she said. I asked her to describe her wardrobe, and then I told her what skirt to wear, what blouse, what shoes, what scarf, and so on—the secret of leadership being the ability to make wholly arbitrary decisions about the running of other people's lives with a certain authority. I told her to put these clothes in a little overnight bag with her toilet articles and her make-up kit, to jump into a taxi and come on over, and we'd just eat simply at home and go to sleep early.

She said she couldn't. Why? She said because, well, she couldn't even think of what to wear in the taxi. She was rapidly disintegrating into catatonia before my very ears.

I asked her if she had a pair of levis. Yes. A pair of tennis shoes? Yes. A sweater? Yes. I told her to put on the levis, the tennis shoes and the sweater, to pack the skirt and blouse and shoes and scarf I'd chosen for her, to walk out the door and hail a cab and come to my apartment. Instantly. At once. She said all right.

By the time she got to my apartment she could barely stand. I took her overnight bag out of her hands. I hugged her and kissed her and led her over to the bed. She sat down, staring somewhat glassily, and I asked her what was wrong.

She shook her head. "I don't know," she said quietly. "It's just that everything's going too fast for me. I can't get so involved again so soon after this other thing I've just been through."

We lay down on the bed and talked for a long while. Then we held each other and we talked some more. And then we made love. This time it was different. It was not a circus this time. I was not an acrobat or a high-wire artist or an animal trainer this time. This time I was a lover. And when it was over I thought I heard her say something and I asked her to repeat it and she shook her head.

"Tell me what you said," I whispered.

"I love you," she said barely audibly.

"I can't hear you," I said.

"I love you," she said a little louder.

"I love you too," I said. We held each other and didn't say anything for a while.

"Tell me what to do," she said eventually.

"What do you mean?" I said.

"Tell me what to do. With my life."

"Move in with me," I said to my utter astonishment. I certainly hadn't planned to say anything like "Move in with me," but that's what came out, and there it was, and after I'd said it I wasn't at all sorry.

"I don't think I can do that," she said.

"Yes, you can," I said. "You can, you want to, and you will." (You can get a little carried away with the leader role sometimes.)

We slept in each other's arms and dreamed all night of everlasting love.

The next day after work Bonnie and I went back to her apartment. She packed up two suitcases full of clothes, her hair dryer, her spice rack and a few more little odds and ends, she said good-by to her three roommates, and then she came to live with me.

19

The nice new excitement of living with a woman, especially with one as beautiful as Bonnie, kept me on an emotional high for weeks. I tried seeing us through the eyes of others and I somehow managed to convince myself we were *both* attractive kids. And, having decided I was attractive, I think I actually *became* somewhat attractive. The way I spoke, the way I stood, the way I walked. I even went out and bought a lot of new clothes to reflect this attractive new image I had of myself: sloppy loafers were replaced by boots, baggy business shirts by tight-fitting Western ones with pearl snaps instead of buttons, shapeless sport coats by tailored bush jackets. I took every pair of pants I owned, including jeans, down to the tailor on the corner to be tapered more tightly than that elderly Jewish gentleman believed was proper. (Maybe the big clothing changeover I just described isn't your idea of attractive, but it worked for me, and that's the point.)

For the first time in my life I dared to talk to women I knew without carefully weeding out all sexuality beforehand. To my amazement, they were more flattered than offended. You mean, I asked myself, I could have had this all along? Nearly fifteen years of dating shot to hell.

Living with Bonnie taught me more about women in the first few weeks than I'd learned in close to thirty years. After we'd outgrown a mutual overcarefulness about things like masking bathroom noises with running water, Bonnie and I dropped our first lines of defense and began to get acquainted. I found out how it felt to take a bath with her (cozy and sweet and, for some odd, dimly remembered reason from childhood, heartbreakingly poignant); how she looked brushing out her hair in front of the mirror (just like in the slow-motion commercials—marvelous); how she looked in a house coat and hair rollers (so awful it was almost enough to make me want to call off the whole arrangement); how she looked sitting on the toilet (silly—so does everyone); how she looked while either dressing or undressing (unbearably desirable); how she looked while absorbed in the process of cooking (serious and solid and motherly); how she looked walking around naked during her period with her little Tampax string hanging down out of her twat (ridiculous—it is not, God forgive me, the most romantic of sights); how it felt to be sick in bed and nursed by her (childish and great); or to have *her* be sick and nurse *her* (fatherly and great for about a day and a half, and after that a gigantic bore); or to spend Sundays together lying around the house and reading the papers and never

quite getting dressed or opening the blinds or getting organized (at once comfortable and full of suffocating dread).

I had never before been very interested in food,
looking upon it as a mildly annoying but necessary
means of alleviating hunger pangs, and regarding
hamburgers, malts, TV dinners, canned ravioli and
Spaghetti-O's as the most direct means to that end.
But Bonnie was a sensational cook and before long
I found myself not only actually looking forward
to dinnertime but taking such things as creamy
white wine sauces entirely for granted. Once that
happens it's hard to get back to Spaghetti-O's, and
you soon find you've upgraded yourself into such
expensive pastimes as the tipping of headwaiters
and the reading of wine lists.

Bonnie and I soon learned how to get on each
other's nerves: I with my absolute inability to
leave the house for any engagement without finding forty last-minute things to take care of and
without making us at least a half hour late to
wherever we were going; she with her absolute inability to keep her clothes or other belongings off
the floor or in any orderly condition whatsoever.
We learned how to have little arguments over nothing at all, and then, to my horror, how to have *big*
ones over nothing at all. I found that my chief con-
cerns at such emotional moments were: (a) to
smooth over all unresolved issues with gross over-
simplifications and pat generalizations, even at per-
il of sealing the wound without cleaning out the
infection, and (b) to keep the neighbors from hear-

ing us. For some reason it seemed terribly important to me that the neighbors should think all was well with our relationship, though there was no reason to suspect my neighbors knew I even *had* a relationship with anyone, since I'd never met them.

The result of most of our arguments was deep depression for us both. Love and living together were not turning out to be the way they were portrayed in the Great American Dream. And although *most* experiences in life had turned out quite different from what we'd been led to expect, this afforded us no perspective. We figured the discrepancy between the myth and the reality was due to our own failings.

Bonnie and I brooded in silence, each probing our individual inadequacies, she lapsing into detached states that I found frighteningly catatonic, I trying to follow her into them and finding myself even more excluded in the process.

One of Bonnie's lesser problems was that she was overqualified for the glorified-secretary job she held, and knew it. She was both scared of trying to improve her lot and contemptuous of herself for *not* trying. I encouraged her, to the point of nagging, to develop her apparent talents in art and design and seek another job in a more satisfying environment. We spent many dreary hours bickering about it.

More to the point, in back of all our argument and all our dread loomed the hungered-for but terrifying steel-jawed trap of wedlock. We referred to it obliquely, fearing to pronounce the actual words, yet talked around it constantly, planning our future together in ambiguous terms:

"If we could live anywhere in the world together —assuming we stayed together, of course—where would you want to live?"

"Well—assuming we stayed together, of course —maybe someplace near the ocean in California. Like Big Sur."

"Yeah? Me too. What kind of house do you think we should have? Assuming we stayed together, I mean."

"Something with lots of glass so we could always see the ocean, and something very enclosed and private so we'd never have to wear any clothes or anything. What kind of car do you think we'd buy? Assuming we stayed together, I mean."

That kind of thing.

Despite the arguments and the hemmed-in feelings there were moments of great joy and closeness: driving a rented car up to a deserted New England beach and re-creating a Smirnoff ad with cocktails in fine glassware on the sand, toasting the setting sun. Walking along the edge of the water in the moonlight and not having to be naked to enjoy it. Then being naked and enjoying that too. Lying in front of the fireplace in a friend's stone house in Connecticut, singing the hopelessly romantic songs of the fifties. Cuddling all night under half a dozen quilts in an old four-poster bed, then getting up very early in the morning for a walk in the woods.

We each developed a healthy respect for the other's intelligence and creative abilities, and despite our frequent tensions, we became not only lovers but incredibly close friends. It sounds corny to put it that way, but we each recognized we were the other's best and possibly only real friend, and we soon found ourselves unable to spend much time apart without feeling lonely and unwhole. No doubt our relationship would have lasted longer had we not placed it in a pressure cooker of such enforced proximity, but there you are.

As a gesture in the direction of increased privacy we decided to look for a larger apartment. We plunged happily into the task of apartment seeking, getting the classified ads from Sunday's *Times* on preceding Wednesdays and racing other young New York couples to the best listings. We knew we were making a further commitment in the direction of permanence, and still we avoided the words wedlock, marriage, husband, wife. The crazy thing is that, though we couldn't speak about marriage, we began to speak about children. We made up names and gave them personalities and soon, to stem the baffling rush of parental longing, we secured two tiny kittens from a friend's cat's litter.

We named the kittens Maurice and Arnold and brought them back to live with us, fussing over the selection of feeding bowls, litter pans, scratching posts and catnip toys like young parents over cribs and strollers. We bemoaned the fact that we couldn't buy little Doctor Dentons for Maurice and Arnold. We decided that when we had real children rather than furry little whiskered ones we would name them Rags and Muffin.

Finally, inevitably, resignedly, we slid backward into talk of marriage—gingerly at first, then with glee at having pronounced the very words and not fallen down screaming and vomiting:

"Oh, my God, *I said it*. I can't believe I actually *said* it. Go on, now *you* say it."

"Say what?"

"You know. What *I* said."

Our mutual narcissism, tempered by shared experience and need, had ripened into love. We giddily told our friends about our plans for marriage, as much to give the idea reality as anything else, and we even called our parents long distance—mine in Chicago, hers in Dayton, Ohio—and told them too.

Both sets of parents knew we were living together (we had not spared them that) and so it could not have been a total surprise. Her parents were delighted. Mine were delighted and apprehensive. They were relieved to learn I was going to end up as a husband after all and not a homosexual. But since they were foreign-born, their memories of concentration camps were not so well buried that they could wholeheartedly embrace the concept of a *shiksa* for a daughter-in-law, a *shiksa* who might, for all one knew, chalk their door in the dead of night with a Mogen David when the pogroms finally got around to Chicago.

We finally found a new apartment we liked, moved in and signed the lease unflinchingly as man and wife. Then Bonnie quit her job and resolved to find one better suited to her abilities. It seemed an ideal time to visit Parent-land and make it all official, and so, leaving Maurice and Arnold with a friend, we flew off to Chicago.

My parents tried so beautifully to accept my Bonnie I could have cried. They allowed us to share the same bedroom, an unheard-of privilege. They fed her full of all the Jewish food in the world, explaining it to her in greater detail than was absolutely necessary:

"Now, Bonnie, here is a nice *bagel* for you. A *bagel*, you see, is a leavened, doughnut-shaped, hard roll, often eaten with cream cheese and *lox*."

"Yes, thank you. I know."

"Here, Bonnie, take some *lox*. *Lox* is a kind of smoked salmon, often eaten with cream cheese on a *bagel*."

When we were ready to leave for Dayton my mother and father both kissed Bonnie and hugged her and told her they were proud and honored to welcome her into our family.

Bonnie's folks in Dayton, though they couldn't quite bring themselves to let us share the same bedroom, were terrific anyway. There were lots of jokes about finally having a son in the family after years of only daughters:

"Well, Dan, I don't know who's more surprised to have a son at our age, Bonnie's mother or myself! What about that, Mildred, aren't you surprised to have a son after all these years?"

I was stuffed with glorious *goyish* food, which happily was not explained to me. I was forced to arm-wrestle with her father and had the sense to lose. All in all it was a pretty happy experience for me, taking part in the great Gentile family gatherings I had seen so much in movies and elsewhere but never been a part of.

But we stayed too long in Dayton, especially in view of our separate sleeping accommodations, and the intimacy we had known and grappled with and learned to thrive on in New York all but evaporated in the warm lap of Bonnie's family. I grabbed for Bonnie in our few private moments and I failed to make contact with her. Beginning to panic, I tore her away from the family hearth one night after dinner under some pretext or other for a drive in the family Oldsmobile.

We drove through the empty streets of Dayton and we tried to talk.

"Bonnie, where are you?"

"I don't know."

"You're not with *me* any more, you know."

"I know."

"It's like you've drifted into some kind of teenaged *Date with Judy* thing, and I'm a guy you necked with in summer camp who's in for the weekend."

"I know. That's what happens to me whenever I come home."

"If we stay here much longer our whole relationship is going to go straight into the toilet."

"I know."

"Is that what you *want?*"

"I don't know."

I parked in a secluded spot and tried to kiss her.

She was cool and unresponsive. Like at the door of her apartment before she ran off to marry the white-socked wonder. I knew I was losing her, losing her beautiful blonde cheerleaderliness, losing her despite our months of wonderful intimacy, and it didn't seem fair. I put my hand under her dress. She pushed it away.

"Why? I said. *"Why?"*

"I don't know. I just don't know."

I pushed her down on the seat of the family Olds and tore off her panties and had carnal knowledge of her in full view of her father's Auto-Kompass and her mother's Trav-L-Mate Kleenex box. And finally, after I'd entered her, long after I'd entered her, she began to respond to me, the old intimacy flickered briefly again, and we knew we had to get back to New York immediately or it was all over between us. We caught a plane back the following day.

Now in our new apartment we kept busy, decorating, settling in. We went to Bloomingdale's and made newlywed noises over curtains and towels and napkins and tablecloths. We horsed with the kittens and cuddled with them in bed. But after the excitement of decorating and settling into the new place died down, the trapped feelings, the arguments and a new sort of restlessness set in.

Now that Bonnie wasn't working we found ourselves in each other's company twenty-four hours a day. Bonnie kept saying she was going out to look for work, but it never happened. She started sleeping later and later, and pretty soon she was hardly getting up at all. The more I pressed her to get up and to get employed, the deeper under the covers she slid.

Our sex life, which had increased markedly upon our return from Dayton, now lapsed through mutual resentments and our respective self-disgust. I found myself looking at strange women in the street who were far less attractive than Bonnie and I hungered for them treacherously. I told myself I was simply bored in bed with Bonnie and I began concocting excuses not to make love to her, avoiding even brushing up against her accidentally under the covers.

And then pretty soon neither of us needed excuses not to have sex. Within days of each other we both developed low-grade cases of non-specific urethritis, and took our pouting genitalia to our respective physicians.

My straight but gentle internist, though he probed my prostate painfully and humiliatingly with rubber-gloved fingers, could find no cause. Innocent of the truth, he suggested I cut down on what he called "sexual acrobatics," eliminate alcohol and spicy foods from my diet. Then he referred me to an elderly WASP urologist with steel engravings of old New England sailing ships on his office walls.

The urologist, feigning distaste, donned rubber gloves and probed some more. He prescribed horrendously expensive capsules to be taken several times a day, and still the urethritis would not be contained. And if I felt degraded by being made to crouch on knees and elbows atop a leather examination table, with my butt in the air like a bitch in heat, while a prissy WASP in a white lab coat and New England sailing ships on his walls shoved his condom-covered finger up my Jewish ass, this was heaven compared to what awaited me next.

I cringe to remember it, but there was a day in my life during which I sat on this selfsame examination table with my pants and underpants down around my dangling ankles, while a sadistic pervert in the guise of a urologist stuck a long hypodermic needle—a hypodermic needle with jagged *threads* spiraling along its length—all the way up my cock and squirted it full of antibiotics. Had he told me what he was about to do I certainly wouldn't have believed him. Once he'd begun it, I was too polite to make him stop. Once he'd finished, he withdrew the needle, pinched the end of my penis between his fingers and affixed a metal clamp.

"Uh, listen," I said, "I don't think I want any more of this."

"The worst is over now," he said. "Just relax and let the antibiotic fluid do its work."

"No, listen," I said, "you don't understand. I really don't *want* any more of this. I mean, the urethritis wasn't really even all that bad. It didn't burn that much and you said yourself it isn't very dangerous, and I really think I liked it better than all of this."

"Just sit still," he said, "or the fluid will leak out and then we'll have to do it all over again." He walked to the door. "Let's try to keep it in there for about ten minutes if we can," he said, opening the door.

"You're *leaving* me?" I said, aghast.

"Well, there's nothing I can do while it's *in* there," he said. "Don't worry, you'll be all right. Just try not to move."

And then he was gone, closing the door swiftly behind him. And there I sat, my trousers dangling, and a large metal clamp attached to the end of my dong.

So this is what it all comes to, I thought. This is what I've been leading up to. French kissing for about eight years, bare tit for another two, petting below-the-waist-inside-the-clothes for a while, and then, when you finally break into the scoring columns—whammo!—a jagged needle up your shlong and a metal clamp at the end of it. They never mentioned *that* in the soppy songs of the fifties.

I sat there feeling ridiculous, watching my watch, berating myself for putting up with such degradation, reasoning that if I didn't know how much the degradation was costing me I would have pulled up my pants and gone home.

There was an impatient knock on the door and in a terrifying flash of clarity I realized that the person who was knocking was someone other than the doctor and, further, was about to enter.

"Hold it!" I hollered. "There's somebody *in* here!"

It was too late. The door opened and a perky blonde nurse pattered into the room. She stopped short and regarded me quizzically. I devoutly wished I was somewhere else.

"Oh," she said. "Isn't Doctor here?"

"No," I said dryly. "Not unless he's crouching under the examination table."

The nurse didn't acknowledge this pleasantry. It was bad enough to even be *talking* to someone with his pants down and a clamp at the end of his wienie without having to laugh at his dumb jokes as well.

"If Doctor comes back in, will you tell him I'm looking for him?"

I nodded miserably. I could see the outlines of her underwear quite plainly through her white nylon uniform and it was very sexy, but I knew I'd never be able to do it even in *fantasy* with someone who'd seen me with my pants down and a clamp on the end of my thing.

The nurse wandered out of the room, leaving the door standing ajar.

"Hey!" I called. "You didn't close the door!"

But she had disappeared. I looked at my watch. It seemed like about three weeks, but the clamp had only been on there for three minutes. If I could just hold out for another seven minutes, maybe the little antibiotic guys swimming around inside me there would spear enough microbes to stop the urethritis.

And now two wonderful things began to happen. The *first* wonderful thing was that I must have moved when the nurse came in and slightly dislodged the clamp, because the antibiotic fluid was beginning to dribble slowly out of my prick and down my leg and into my pants. The *second* wonderful thing was that people—other patients, other nurses, and general passers-by—were beginning to walk down the hallway past the office in which I sat, they were noticing that the door was ajar and they were all peering in as they passed.

I didn't know what to do. If I took off the clamp, the rest of the fluid would spurt out and old Torquemada would have to do the whole thing all over again. If I tried to hold the clamp in place as I got down off the examination table and walked to the door to close it, I would risk tearing off the end of my prick and probably also send people screaming out into the street. So, not knowing what else to do, I just sat there and watched the world go by and didn't do a thing. I suppose I should at least have waved.

Eight minutes later the doctor came back into the room, unclamped me and asked why the door was open. I thought of telling him I was an exhibitionist and had an uncontrollable urge to display myself, but I didn't. I was afraid he might believe me.

Maddened by equivalent pussy experiences, Bonnie was at least temporarily snapped out of her catatonia. I used this opportunity to encourage her to put together a portfolio of her art work and designs and do something about job hunting. She kept muttering that she wasn't good enough, but I nagged her until she did it.

What she had when she got through were about

a dozen very impressive pen-and-ink sketches and about a dozen spreads I'd urged her to put together from ads we'd torn out of newspapers and magazines: on the left-hand page of each spread was an existing mediocre ad, on the right-hand page was how she would have redesigned it. It was by no means a professional portfolio, but it was an indication to anyone who cared to give it more than a cursory glance that there was a person who could, with a bit of instruction and experience, become a pretty fair little art director in a short period of time.

We made up a list of ad agencies I thought might at least give her an interview, and I called up an old advertising buddy of mine named Mort, who agreed to see her right away. We picked out her most alluring combination of clothes, I practically dressed her myself, and soon Bonnie was running out the door with her portfolio under her arm, off to her first interview in Ad-land.

One hour later she was back, clearly dazed.

"How did it go, hon?" I said. "Did he at least give you a list of people to call?"

She shook her head. "He did better than that," she said. "He hired me."

"He *did?*"

She nodded. "He said he loved everything I'd done. He wants me to start tomorrow."

I gave a great whoop of joy, and then we both did a little dance of victory around the room and hugged and kissed and suddenly everything between us was all right again.

That night we went out to a moderately expensive restaurant I knew in order to celebrate, and we were so peppy and looked so great and happy and in love that the headwaiter sent a complimentary bottle of wine over to our table. I don't ask you to believe that such a thing could happen in a tough, tired place like New York, but it did, and I don't suppose it will ever happen again to me or to anyone else who isn't Jacqueline Kennedy, but that night it happened.

"You know," Bonnie said to me in bed that night as we made love, mindless of peepee problems, "I owe it all to you. I never could have gotten out of my depression and put together that portfolio and gotten that job without you."

"Nonsense," I said with becoming modesty, "all I did was nag you."

"No," she said, "you made me into something better than I was before. Just like Pygmalion. And I love you a lot. You know, I'm really happy now that we're getting married. I wasn't too thrilled with that idea for a while there, but I am now. We're really going to be okay from now on, aren't we?"

"We're going to be perfect," I said.

"And we're not going to end up like other married couples either, are we?"

"How do you mean?"

"Oh, you know. All fighty and icky and fooling around with other people's wives and husbands and stuff."

"No, I don't think we'll end up like that," I said.

241

"Good. I'd really hate it if we did."

Maurice and Arnold chased each other across the bed and we caught them and held them and nuzzled our noses in their warm furry little bellies.

"As soon as we get married," Bonnie said, "we're going to have to start investigating private nursery schools for Maurice and Arnold."

"Yes," I said, "one can't begin too early to plan a youngster's education, can one? As Horace Heidt used to say, it's better to build boys than to mend men."

"But which school do you think is really *right* for them?" she said. "I mean, do you feel Maurice and Arnold are more your Bank Street School type or your Dalton type, your Little Red Schoolhouse or your basic Brearly?"

"I would say that Maurice and Arnold are definitely your French Lycée type," I said.

Maurice and Arnold, bored with human inanities, wriggled out of our embrace and ran off to chase each other around the apartment again.

"What do you think they'd do at one of those fancy progressive nursery schools," I said, "if we showed up for the interview with two kittens in a cat carrier and introduced them as our sons?"

"I don't think it would faze those people in the least," she said, giggling at the prospect.

"Me either," I said. "In fact, depending on how large a pledge we were willing to make to the building fund, I'll bet they'd enroll them."

We cracked each other up and then we hugged a lot and I really thought we were okay again.

Bonnie's new job at Mort's agency was perfect. Not only did they let her do actual layouts for their clients after the first two weeks, they were simply insane about her personally. (I don't imagine that her fantastic looks hurt things either.) Where formerly she had been an unappreciated glorified secretary in an office full of ladies, now she was a pretty art director in an office full of horny men. (I'd made a special point to Mort about how Bonnie and I were living together and engaged to be married and everything, just to be on the safe side.)

When Bonnie started working again, so did I. I did an incredible amount of writing and I started selling it at a furious rate, so we were in great shape, both financially and emotionally. We even stopped having non-specific urethritis. We still hadn't set a date for our wedding—we weren't yet in *that* great shape emotionally—but we'd been together for about ten months at this point and we figured we'd legalize our relationship by the end of our first year.

One day Bonnie came home from work with a peculiar expression on her face, the kind that if someone is wearing it and you don't say something like: "Hey, what's that peculiar expression on your face for?" they think you're being hostile.

"Hey," I said, "what's that peculiar expression on your face for?"

She started to laugh in anticipation of what she was going to tell me. "Listen," she said, "have I ever mentioned a guy in the office by the name of Louis?"

"Louis? No, I don't think so. Why?"

"Well, anyway, there's this guy in the office and his name is Louis, and I think he has a crush on me."

"Oh?" I said. "What makes you think that?"

"Well," she said, "he s very self-conscious and shy and everything when he's around me, not like all the other guys in the office. And also he keeps asking me to lunch."

"He does?"

"Yeah."

"Doesn't he know about us?" I said.

"Oh, sure. He knows. He just keeps asking anyway."

"And what do you say when he asks you?"

"Well, that I can't go, of course. But it doesn't seem to stop him."

"I see," I said. "Tell me, what, ah, does this Louis person *look* like?"

She burst out laughing again. "Oh, God, you're not *jealous* are you? Jealous of poor *Louis?*"

"Well, I don't *think* I am, but why is that such a big yock?"

"You'd know how funny it was if you knew Louis."

"Why? What is he, a dwarf?"

"No, but he's not very attractive He's all bald, for one thing, and for another he's about eighty years old."

"What is he, the janitor?"

"No, an account executive."

"You have eighty-year-old account executives in

your agency? On what account, Polident?"

"Well, he's not really *eighty*. He's more like, I don't know, fifty-five or sixty or something. And he's completely bald. I mean he shaves his *head*, for God's sake."

"So? So does Yul Brynner. Lots of ladies find him attractive, too."

"Well, I can see this is all wasted on you. Here I thought I'd make you laugh and instead you're some kind of old grouch all of a sudden."

"I *want* to laugh, honey, but all you've told me so far is that an old bald man is hot for you. Now either he's in for a broken heart, or else *I* am—and neither one of those prospects strikes me as being particularly riotous."

"Boy," she said disgustedly, "remind me to tell you something funny *again* sometime."

A few days later she came home with the same dumb expression on her face.

"I guess you're not going to think this is funny either," she said, "but I've got to tell you anyway."

"Shoot," I said.

"You know what Louis did today?"

"What?"

"Gave me a single red American Beauty rose."

I nodded.

"Do you think that's funny?" she said.

"Not particularly," I said. "Why, do you?"

"No," she said, "I don't guess I really think it's funny either, come to think of it."

"You don't."

"No I mean, I guess it's actually sort of sweet.

Corny, I mean, but also sweet."

"Ah. And what did you say to him?"

"When he gave me the rose?"

"Yes."

She raised her eyebrows. "I said thank you," she said.

A couple of days later she came home and walked over to where I was sitting at the typewriter and dropped something into my lap.

"What's this?" I said.

"A book, obviously. *Louis* gave it to me. Take a look at it, I think it's kind of sweet."

I looked at the book. Then I looked up at her. "Louis gave you *A Friend Is Someone Who Likes You?*"

"Yes. Why?"

"That pervert!"

"What are you talking about? It's a sweet little book. It's a *children's* book. What are you talking about?"

A Friend Is Someone Who Likes You is not *either* a children's book. *A Friend Is Someone Who Likes You* is what every horny old man over the age of fifty gives to every pretty girl under the age of twenty-five he *meets.* You can't even *buy* that book unless you're a horny old man over the age of fifty and you can prove to the salesperson at the bookstore that you're giving it to a girl under the age of twenty-five—they won't even *sell* it to you."

"I think you're being really horrible and grouchy and dumb. Just because a poor, silly old bald man in my office likes me well enough to give me a sweet little book is no—"

"You think you're the only girl he's ever given a copy of that book to? You really think so? Sneak into his office someday after he leaves and look around. I'll bet you find an entire *carton* of *A Friend Is Someone Who Likes You.* I'll bet he buys them direct from the publisher by the fucking *gross.*"

She marched out of the room. I had gone too far. I went after her and caught her in my arms and apologized to her. And although she tried to wriggle away from me like Maurice and Arnold, I told her I'd hold her till she accepted my apology and finally she did.

"Honey," I said, "I'm sorry I made fun of Louis and of his gift to you. I know it's flattering to a woman to be paid attention to and to be given things by an admirer, and I'm glad you feel flattered, I really am. And I'm *mainly* glad that what he's giving you are only cliché gifts like a single red rose or a copy of *A Friend Is Someone Who Likes You,* and I'm even gladder that it's just an old bald man who's giving them to you. Because if they were really great original gifts and if he were really some terrific young guy, I'd really be in a lot of trouble. I mean, sometimes I really get awfully afraid of losing you. If that ever happened it would be just terrible."

She kissed me sweetly and held my head against her breasts and I think she was truly touched at my fear of losing her.

"Don't worry about losing me," she whispered. "I could never leave you. I wouldn't even know what to *do* without you."

It was almost worth my outburst.

We didn't talk too much about Louis for the next week or so, but then one day the Hairless Wonder struck again.

"Guess what Louis gave me today?" said Bonnie.

"Wait now, let me think. I know. A cherry that has no stone?"

"No. Seriously. What?"

"A chicken that has no bone?"

"No, come on now. Guess."

"A ring that has no end? A baby with no cry-en"?"

"Come *o-on*."

"Okay. What?"

"A thing from Tiffany's."

"A *what?*"

"A thing from Tiffany's. A trinket."

"A *ring* trinket?"

"No, silly. Just a trinket. A pin thing."

"I trust you gave it back to him?"

"How could I have given it back to him?"

"By opening his hand, placing the trinket inside of it and then pulling your own hand away."

"Oh, I couldn't do that."

"Why not?"

"Because. It would have hurt his feelings."

"I see," I said. "Well now, does this mean you two kids are going steady or what?"

She made a face at me. "Louis doesn't think of me that way," she said. "You don't understand about him."

"I understand *perfectly* about him," I said. "It's *you* who doesn't understand about him. Why do *you* think old men buy young women presents?"

"Maybe *other* old men buy young women presents to get them into bed, but that's not why Louis does. I'll tell you something he asked me and then maybe you'll understand about him."

"Okay."

"Well, Louis turns out to be this very wealthy person, and he has this big farm and everything in Connecticut . . ."

"Yes . . ."

"And he asked me if we wanted to sort of come up there and visit him this weekend."

"If *we* wanted to? You mean he invited me too?"

"Yes."

"He invited both of us up to his farm *together?*"

"*Yes.*"

"Good God."

"Well? What do you think about Louis *now?*"

"I think that Louis is either a masochist and a damned fool or else he is the sneakiest, most dangerous man I've ever heard of. Let me ask you something. Are you at all attracted to him?"

She shrugged.

"Are you or aren't you?" I said.

"Not really. It's just that he's so, you know, so attentive and . . . persistent and everything."

At this very moment old Louis was doubtless poking through his shopworn bag of tricks, trying to decide which of his suave collection of chestnuts to lay on Bonnie next. Well, what shall it be this time, the old carriage-ride-through-Central-Park routine? The rowboat-ride-in-the-Lagoon? The time-honored trip-on-the-Staten-Island-Ferry? The ever popular brunch-in-the-Edwardian-Room-of-the-Plaza-Hotel? Or perhaps another sure-fire book—*The Prophet*, *The Little Prince*, or should we break open a fresh carton of *Happiness Is a Warm Puppy?*

The shotgun approach to romance: send out a hundred single red American Beauty roses, a hundred copies of *A Friend Is Someone Who Likes You*, and a certain calculable percentage of recipients will blushingly topple into your bed. It's about as personal as a newspaper horoscope or a message in a fortune cookie. YOU ARE A SENSITIVE PERSON . . . YOU HAVE SUFFERED . . . THERE IS A SIDE OF YOU THAT NOBODY KNOWS . . . YOU ARE WARM AND LOVING IF GIVEN THE CHANCE TO EXPRESS IT . . . ONCE SOMEBODY HURT YOU IN A WAY THAT THEY AREN'T EVEN AWARE OF BUT THAT YOU WILL NEVER FORGET . . . YOU SELDOM REVEAL THE REAL YOU EVEN TO THOSE WHO ARE CLOSEST TO YOU . . . YOU WILL KNOW GREAT HAPPINESS AND GREAT SADNESS . . .

Who *wouldn't* feel that most of those applied to him? Sentiments like stretch socks: One Size Fits All. It works, though. And the reason it works is that everybody in the entire world has always thought of himself as sensitive, vulnerable, misunderstood, a secret pussycat—from Albert Schweitzer to your neighborhood heavy appliance repairman to Jack the Ripper—just as everybody in the world thinks he has good taste, a good sense of humor and winning ways in bed. In our secret hearts we're all the same person. If we had to rely on everyone's image of himself for identification, we'd be indistinguishable from one another. Nobody would ever get the right clothes back from the laundry.

"Tell me," I said to Bonnie, "do you have any desire at all to go out with Louis?"

She shrugged. "No. Not really."

"Are you sure? Because if you do, and if he keeps on pressing you like this, and if you start being tempted to go out with him and feel you can't because of me, then maybe you're going to start resenting me. Resenting being chained to me."

"*Chained* to you. I'm not *chained* to you, for God's sake," she said. "I could leave here any time I wanted to."

I took an involuntary inward breath. "Yes, I know that," I said. "That's why I'd like to know for certain that you don't have any latent desire to go out with this person."

"Well," she said, "I don't *think* I do."

"Good," I said.

"But then, he hasn't really asked me."

I looked at her carefully for a moment, and then wisely decided to say nothing.

The next day she came home and said in this

funny voice: "Guess what?"

"He *asked* you," I said.

She nodded.

"Well, well, well. You still think old Louis has only platonic plans for you?"

She shook her head.

"Well, what did you tell him?"

"I told him . . . that I didn't know."

I began to feel slightly sick. "What is it that you don't know?" I said, beginning to blow my cool, "whether you want to go out with a horny old man, a horny old professional giver of banal gifts to other men's fiancées? Is that what you don't know?"

It was the wrong tack, definitely the wrong tack to take. I shifted gears smoothly, thinking fast.

"Look, hon," I said. "A man pays attention to you. You're very flattered. He asks you to go out with him. You're even more flattered. You wonder what it would be like to go out with him, but you feel you can't because you're living with someone else. Well"—I paused for dramatic value—"I think you *ought* to go out with him."

"You do?"

"Why not? We're free agents. We're not chained to one another, you said so yourself. If you think you want to go out with him, I say go ahead and do it."

She said nothing.

"Do you think you want to?" I said.

She shook her head. "It's so confusing," she said. "I'm not *sure*."

"Even if you're *not* sure, I say go out with him.

Satisfy your curiosity. Find out that an evening with Louis isn't necessarily any more exciting than an evening with me."

"Well," she said, "if you really think I *ought* to . . ."

"Absolutely," I said. "Don't give it another thought. And if while you're out with him he should ask you to go to bed with him, and if you should feel you might like to—no, not should you *feel* you might like to, should you even *suspect* you'd like to—I say go ahead and do that too."

She was staring at me with great interest. "What makes you think I want to go to bed with him?" she said.

"Well, I don't know that you do. But you must have at least wondered at *some* point during all of this what it might be like to be in bed with him. And if so, I would much rather you went ahead and did it, went and got it out of your system, went and found out he's nothing special, found out he's just another guy with just another dork, than have you feel you couldn't do it because you were living with me and then begin to have *fantasies* about it, have it become some kind of *fixation* or something."

"Well," she said, "that's really very . . . generous of you. Very . . . open-minded."

"Not at all, not at all," I said. "As a matter of fact, I think the whole experience of going out with someone else will be good for *both* of us."

"*Both* of us," she said.

"Well, you certainly didn't think I was going to

sit home alone and *wait* for you, did you?"

"Well, no, I suppose not."

"Fine. What night shall we plan to make it then?"

"You certainly seem anxious to get the whole thing going," she said.

"I just want to make sure we can both do it the same night, that's all."

She nodded. "Who were you thinking of going out with?" she said.

"What's the difference?" I said.

"No difference. I just wondered."

"I see," I said. "So tell me, what night did Louis ask you out for?"

"Friday."

"Friday. Good. Excellent. Friday it is, then."

I had truthfully been hoping that giving Bonnie the actual freedom to go out with Louis would make the whole thing seem less attractive and cause her to chicken out or lose interest in it. Negative psychology, and the Strongest Chain Is *No* Chain, and all that.

Well, I'd lost that gamble, but perhaps it was just as well. Perhaps spending an entire evening in the company of the sort of man who bought girls single red roses and copies of *A Friend Is Someone Who Likes You* would cure her forever of wanting to go out with anyone else. In any case, I now had not the opportunity but the *obligation* not only to go out with another woman on Friday night but to get laid as well, it seemed. I didn't know whether or not Bonnie was going to end up in bed with

Louis, but I didn't feel I could take the chance of being one down on her if she did and I didn't.

I called up a lady named Charlotte, the same one I'd gone to bed with the night after I'd first made love to Bonnie, the night Bonnie was too tired to see me, and I made a date with her. I felt it was somehow fitting to choose this lady, in addition to which she was about the only one I still knew well enough to call.

There was something terribly perverse about showering and getting dressed with Bonnie on Friday evening, knowing we were both getting ready to go out to dinner with and possibly even to bed with someone else. We felt great danger in what we were doing, but we found the danger irresistible and fascinating. We kidded about playing out an American version of *Les Liaisons Dangereuses*.

It had been arranged that Louis would meet Bonnie outside our apartment in his car rather than come inside. The prospect of the fatherly old gent picking up his date in the home she shared with her fiancé was too black a switch on the conventional American dating experience, even for sophisticates like us.

At last the agreed-upon hour arrived. The doorbell rang, Bonnie put on her coat and headed for the door.

"Have a nice time, hon," I said.

"You too," she said.

"And remember, if you feel like going to bed with him—"

"Oh, be *quiet*," she said. She left.

What kind of a man was this Louis, I wondered, this bald old fart with hairy young fart inclinations? How much of his obsession with Bonnie had to do with the fact that she belonged to me?

Perhaps I should have had the courage to confront him when he called for her. Gone to the door and invited him in for a drink while Bonnie went to put on her lipstick and stuff.

Sit down, Louis, sit down. Bonnie will be ready in just a minute. Well now, what'll you have? Cutty on the rocks with a splash of the old *agua?* Fine. Well now, Louis, Bonnie's been telling me a lot about you of late. Glad to have the chance of meeting you in person. I hope you won't think me an old snoop, but I generally like to meet the young men who come by to take my little girl out. You'll forgive me, Louis, but I hadn't realized how old a fella you were. Bonnie never mentioned your age specifically. What are you—sixty? sixty-five? seventy? I see you're a bald fella. Oh, now don't get me wrong, Louis. I don't have anything against Bonnie's going out with a bald fella, not even with an *old* bald fella. Not at all. As a matter of fact, I happen to know several old bald fellas quite well, and they're all swell guys. They say that baldness is a sign of virility. That true in your case, Louis? Are you, heh heh, still a pretty virile guy? Still able to get it up, Louis, even with the young honeys? Eh? Just kidding ya, Louis. That's none of my business, of course. That's between you and Bonnie.

Well, Louis, I think you'll like my Bonnie. Yes, sir, I think Bonnie will show you a real good time.

Got a terrific set of jugs on her, that little girl, and a cooz that's just as tight as a twelve-year-old's. *Say,* I hope I'm not *embarrassing* you by talking about Bonnie's cooz, am I? Matter of fact, she's been having a little trouble in there of late, Louis, but it's nothing to worry about. It shouldn't give you any trouble. If it does, I can recommend one hell of a great weewee doctor. Terrific fella, same as yourself, with engravings of old sailing ships on his walls. Hell, he'll fix you up real good in no time at all. Little hypodermic needle full of penicillin up your old cock-a-rooney and you'll be good as new.

Whoops—here comes the little lady now. Okay, kids, don't stay out too late. Good meeting ya, Louis. Have fun now, you two, ya hear? And don't do anything *I* wouldn't do!

I went to pick up Charlotte, and I tried to keep my mind off Bonnie and Louis and what they might be doing together later on. I poured myself some of Charlotte's scotch and then I jumped her.

It was a lusty, spirited, juicy, yet ultimately joyless fuck and it wore me out. The adulterous nature of the act excited me more than usually at the beginning and depressed me more than usually at the end. We dressed and went out to eat and I couldn't keep my mind off of Bonnie and Louis. I drank stingers all through dinner and after that I took Charlotte back home and sat down with her and somewhat mechanically went about the task of making the time pass. Because although I did enjoy Charlotte's company, the evening was over, had really been over at the instant grudgefucking moment of entry into her vulva, and I was as eager to be gone as I was not to be the first one home.

I stayed another hour and then I left. When I got back to the apartment it was well after 2:00 A.M., but Bonnie wasn't home yet. It was too late for her still to be out eating, and so she was now either on her way back or else in bed with Louis. At this very moment he could be tugging down her panties, spreading her sweet chops and thrusting his dirty-old-bald-fart dork into her slippery little pussy, the pussy that was rightfully mine but out on loan, and she could be whipping her head back and forth and saying the weeny weeny little far-away no-no-no's she'd said with me, ready to tell him when he asked that it was all right, not to pay any attention to her, that it was only a noise she made.

Of course it was equally possible that she was neither in bed with Louis *nor* on her way home, that she was merely waiting a bit longer before coming back, being as eager as I not to be the first one home. Maybe she was even staying out late to make me squirm for seeming so willing to go through with this adventure in the first place, for calling Charlotte so speedily and making a date with her.

Around 4:00 A.M. I heard the key in the door and Bonnie tiptoed into the apartment. She was almost two hours up on me.

"Well," I said, hiding my annoyance, "how did it go?"

"Okay, I guess," she said.

"Did you get laid?" I said.

She turned and looked at me with great contempt. "No," she said, "I did not."

"Really?" I said. "I thought you were going to. *I* did."

It was a crude thing to have said, let alone done, and I'd said the crude thing crudely, but I thought I caught a faint glimmer of interest in her face.

I followed her into the bathroom and quizzed her about her date like some ambivalent parent. She told me that they'd talked all night, that Louis was far more intelligent and sensitive and complex than she'd thought, that he never even suggested that they go to bed, but that if he had done so she might have gone along with it.

Things were getting more and more out of hand every moment, and there was nothing I could think of to do except continue along the perverse line I'd started on.

"Well," I said, "as I told you before, if you have any curiosity about what he's like in bed, I think you ought to go ahead and find out."

"Well then, perhaps I will," she said.

"Well then, go ahead," I said.

"Perhaps I will," she said.

"Go ahead, then," I said.

We got into bed and Bonnie turned her back and composed herself for sleep. We hadn't been so far apart, I thought, since our visit to her folks in Dayton. Perhaps, as I had in Dayton, I could physically force the return of our intimacy. I snuggled up to her and began to caress her back.

"I'm very tired," she said. "I'd really like to go to sleep."

"I just wanted to cuddle a little," I said. "What's wrong with that?"

"You don't want to cuddle, you want to screw."

"Well then, what's wrong with that?"

"I told you. I'm tired. Besides, haven't you had enough sex for one night?"

"Oho! So *that's* what this is."

"No," she said tiredly, "that's *not* what this is."

"Oh, come on," I siad.

"No, really," she said, "it's not. I'm not jealous. I thought I might be if you went to bed with her, but I'm not. I almost wish I *were.*"

"What's *that* supposed to mean?" I said.

"It doesn't matter," she said. "It's very late, I'm very tired, and I'd like to get some sleep. I've had a very long evening."

"Yes," I said assily, "chatting with Louis must be tiring."

"You can say all the rude things you like about Louis," she said. "They don't matter at all."

"I'm sorry I said that. I'm sure Louis is a very intelligent, interesting person to talk to."

"He is," she said.

"What did he talk to you about, for the most part?"

"What's the difference?" she said.

"I really want to know. I want to know what made old Louis so interesting to talk to all night."

"We talked about a great many things," she said.

"You might not have found them as interesting as I did."

"Oh? Why not?"

"Because," she said. "Because of your lack of . . . social consciousness."

"My *what?*"

"Your social awareness. Your involvement in the society in which you live. How involved are you in the great social issues of the day?"

"What are you talking about?" I said. "I've gone to as many peace rallies as you have. I've written as many vile letters to the President as you have. I've sent as many two-dollar checks to the Negroes and the Vietnamese and the Biafrans and the Indians and the unwed mothers and the paralyzed girl who draws the crappy Christmas cards with the pencil between her teeth as you have."

"Don't use me as your yardstick," she said.

"Why not?"

"Because I'm as guilty as you are in that area," she said.

"Then why criticize *me* for it?"

"Because. It's your *fault* I'm not more involved. You *feed* my lack of social consciousness."

"How's old *Louis's* social consciousness?" I said. "Pretty well developed, I suppose?"

"You'd be surprised," she said.

"Not at all," I said. "I wouldn't be the slightest *bit* surprised. I'm sure he marched and demonstrated and sat-in for the entire Spanish-American War. Those advertising executives are the biggest radicals in the world. It's a known fact. The goddam F.B.I. has been tapping phones on Madison Avenue since the day the Czar was overthrown in Russia."

"As I said before, it doesn't make the slightest difference to me what you say about him."

"I know," I said miserably. "Listen, are you really planning to go out with him again?"

"I imagine so."

"I see," I said. "Well, that's fine with me, and I'm all for it, but I'm afraid it's not going to happen while you're living with *me*."

"What are you saying?" she said.

"What I am saying," I said, and then my voice broke and I had to continue a lot more haltingly. "What I am saying, Bonnie, is that . . . that I don't want you to go out with Louis again. What I am saying is that I want us to go on living together and I want us to . . . try and remember how much in love we used to be, and I am saying that I want you to either make the commitment to our relationship now of giving up going out with Louis and anyone else, or, if you can't do that, then maybe it would be better if you . . . well, if you went back to your old apartment and . . . thought things over for a couple of days."

There was a long silence and then she said: "Well, in that case, I guess maybe I'd better go back to my old apartment."

I suddenly became ill. "Then maybe you'd better," I said.

"Is it all right if I don't leave until morning?" she said.

I nodded, then broke for the bathroom. When I had finished puking my guts out, I washed up and came back to bed. Bonnie was crying.

"Bonnie honey," I said, gathering her up in my arms. "What is it?"

"Oh, it's so sad," she said.

"Yes," I said, "it is."

"Leaving little Maurice and Arnold," she said, "I can't stand it."

20

The next day she left. I watched her pack until she told me I was making her nervous and she asked me to go for a walk. She said not to come back till she was gone. She said she'd call me in a couple of days and tell me what she had decided to do. She had the beginnings of a truly rotten cold and she appeared to be savoring it as some kind of penance for what was to come.

I went outside and took my walk. I told myself that she was just going away for a couple of days to think things out, that she would realize how much she really needed me while she was gone (hadn't she once said she wouldn't even know what to *do* without me?), that she would come back to me and we would start all over again. I told myself it was actually a good thing that this was happening and that when she came back to me and we started all over again it would be on an even firmer basis. I told myself I was full of shit. Bonnie my love, Bonnie my future wife, was running off with her socially aware octogenarian and she was never coming back to me.

What an ass I'd been to think I could bluff her out of Louis. What a shmuck to think that giving someone the freedom to do what they were tempted to do would make them lose interest in doing it. I'd probably *stimulated* that interest more than anything else. If I hadn't made such a big deal out of Louis and his ass-holic gifts, she probably wouldn't even have taken him seriously. I had practically thrown her into his bed with my shmucky attempts at worldliness and sophistication. Who the fuck was I to be fooling around with sophisticated sexual intrigues anyway? I wasn't Jean-Paul Belmondo or Marcello Mastroianni, I was a Jewish kid from Chicago who couldn't get laid till he was twenty-three and who got nervous and threw up a lot.

I went back to the apartment an hour later and Bonnie was indeed gone. She had taken a few changes of clothing in a suitcase and a shopping bag, but that was about all. The apartment was terrible without her. I walked through it slowly, and I realized there wasn't a single thing, a single picture or article of furniture or kitchen utensil or anything else, that we hadn't picked out together and that didn't have a heart-cracking memory hanging from it like a price tag. Maurice and Arnold scampered into the room, realized they hadn't had breakfast yet and began rubbing up against me, mewing piteously to be fed. I took a can of cat food out of the cabinet under the sink and started to open it, and then I remembered our idea of trying to enroll them in a private nursery school and I began to cry.

Having finished with that, I decided to be very mature and very practical and efficient about the whole thing. The roughest part was going to be getting through the next few days, and the only way I was going to be able to do that was to cut down on the number of spikes of emotional impalement which were scattered all over the apartment. I went around and gathered up all the pictures of Bonnie I could find and all of her lingerie and stuff and I shoved it into a trunk where I wouldn't have to look at it. Then I sat down on a chair next to the window and didn't do another thing for three days except go to the shrink, and he was no help at all.

On the third day Bonnie called. I tried to keep my voice normal and I asked how she was. She said she was all right, her cold had gotten much worse, and she wanted to come by and pick up some stuff. I said sure.

When she arrived I was terribly nonchalant. Looking at her caused me violent physical pain, but I could not possibly have been more nonchalant. I asked her if I could help carry her things outside and get her a cab, and she said thanks anyway, that Louis was outside with the car and it might be awkward. I said certainly, I understood, and I became so nonchalant I could scarcely move.

"Well," she said at the door, her arms full of clothes and boxes of hair rollers and hair dryers and things, "this ought to hold me for a while."

"Yes," I said.

"Well, so long," she said. "See you soon."

Then she left.

See you soon. What could that mean? Could it possibly mean that she was coming back to *see me soon?* Could it conceivably mean that she was having second thoughts about leaving me and was in the process of deciding to come back and live with me?

No, of course not. Shmuck. If she were even considering the possibility of coming back to me, then why would she have taken more clothes and boxes of hair rollers and her hair dryer with her? (To think I'd once been unable to stand the sight of her in hair rollers. I would *kill* to have her back in my house in hair rollers.)

This ought to hold me for a while. What could that mean? Maybe what it meant was that she was only taking enough things to *hold her for a while* —that she expected to be coming back to me soon and therefore didn't need more than a few bare necessities.

I rushed to the telephone and called up three close friends in succession who knew about our breakup and, in perfect high school fashion, I related to them every word that Bonnie had uttered and asked them for their interpretations. I repeated each of her lines, giving them a different emphasis here, a different twist there, a different spin, a different body English, and, depending on the reading I gave them, Bonnie at the time she'd originally

268

spoken these lines had either been forcibly restraining herself from leaping into my arms or else she'd just finished giving Louis head in the car.

A few days later she came by again to get more of her things. I watched in silence as she stuffed several shopping bags full of clothes.

"I still haven't been able to get everything," she said. "There's so much here."

"I know," I said.

"I'll have to come back some Saturday with a truck or something," she said. "Listen, do you mind very much if I take back my spice rack?"

I shrugged. "It's yours," I said. "You might as well take it."

She went to the kitchenette wall and lifted her spice rack off the pegboard.

"There's a lot of things we bought together which I suppose we'll have to divide up one of these days," she said. "I don't really feel up to it at the moment, though."

"Neither do I."

"There's one thing, though, that I'd sort of like to take back with me now if you don't mind."

"What's that?"

"Well, I suppose this is going to sound kind of dumb and petty, but if you'll remember, the mop was something I brought with me when I moved in with you."

"The *mop?*"

"Yes. Do you mind very much if I take it?"

I sighed, then shook my head. "Go ahead," I said, "take the mop. What the hell."

"Thanks."

She went to the broom closet and got out the mop. Then, picking up the spice rack and the shopping bags, she started for the door. I hustled over and opened it for her.

"By the way," I said, "how's Louis?"

"Louis? Oh, he's okay. Why?"

"Are things between you working out okay?"

"Yeah. Pretty much."

"You don't think you'll be . . . moving in with him or anything, do you?"

"I don't really know," she said. "I mean, he hasn't even asked me."

"I see," I said.

"How about you?" she said. "Have you found someone to go out with?"

"Sort of," I said.

"Is it anything . . . ?" Then she shook her head.

"Is it anything *what*—serious?" I said.

"I'm sorry I asked that," she said. "It's none of my business."

"Sure it is. Sure it's your business. We can still care what happens to each other, can't we? No, it's *not* anything serious. I mean, not at this point, anyway."

"I see," she said.

There was an uncomfortable pause. Each of us seemed to be considering what to say next.

"I'm leaving you the mop," she said abruptly, and thrust it into my hands.

"What for?" I said.

"I can't take it away from you. It isn't right."

"What do I care about a goddamned mop? Here, take it." I thrust it back at her.

"No," she said, pushing it toward me. "You take it. I don't even know why I asked you for it."

"No," I said stubbornly, "*you* take it."

"No," she said, her voice suddenly charged with emotion, "*I want you to have this mop.*"

"I don't want it," I said. "*I will not have this mop in my home.*"

I planted it firmly in her hands. We stood there for a moment, seething with emotions neither of us knew what to do with. Then Bonnie accepted the mop, burst into tears and tore out of the apartment.

About a week later Bonnie called me again. Once more I chatted with her as casually as if she were some lady I'd met once at a cocktail party rather than someone who was tearing my guts out. I kept waiting for her to reveal the purpose of her call—that she was coming over to get some more of her things or something like that—but she never did. And so the conversation just petered out and was over.

I immediately called my three advisers and recited the conversation back to them, with various inflections and shadings. The consensus was that she was Making Overtures. And sixty-six and two thirds per cent of them felt I should call her back and ask her out to dinner. I did so, she accepted the invitation, and I was hopeful for the first time since she'd left.

I plotted out every move of the evening like a bank robbery—where to go, what route to take, what to say, what to avoid saying, exactly what tone to strike in what I said and did. I reasoned (brilliantly, I felt) that she would be expecting me to take her to one of our old, softly lit, romantic hangouts and make some cheap attempt to stir up old memories. I faked her out completely by taking her to a place that we had not only never been to together but that was not even romantic. What I now lacked in atmosphere I'd more than made up for, I felt, in the element of surprise.

Conversation during dinner was not quite the effervescent tour de force I would have wished. This was partially due to the fact that the very *sight* of food was keeping me perilously close to the brink of unconsciousness. Nevertheless, I downed several stingers and not only didn't throw up all over her (which would have been a bad tactical error), but I even managed to get a few forkfuls of food into my mouth and down my throat.

I told her how upset I was about the war of late, how pissed I was about the way the Negroes and the Indians were being treated, and I indicated that I was toying with the possibility of volunteering for some menial but meaningful job in one of the more disgusting ghetto areas of the city. This was not idle talk—I had already made several inquiries and was nearly prepared to take such a step in the desperate hope it would bring Bonnie rushing back to me, screaming: "You're relevant, you're relevant, I love you!"

After dinner I decided that my brilliance in selecting such an unromantic restaurant to dine in now allowed me to reverse my field and take her for after-dinner drinks to a moody little bar in the top of the Beekman Tower which we'd frequented when we first started dating. She realized what I was up to, of course, and she even agreed to go there with me, but it did not turn out to be one of the twelve best ideas of the year. It developed that the Beekman Tower was undergoing extensive renovation, and instead of intimate soft lighting we had several naked bulbs hanging from utility cords overhead and we also had a fine rain of plaster dust continually falling into our hair and our drinks from a gigantic hole in the ceiling.

I took her back to the apartment she shared with her three girl friends, I gave her a chaste little closed-mouth kiss outside her door, and we were right back to where we were when we'd first started dating—it was exactly as though the whole living together as man and wife for nearly a year had never even happened.

I went home more depressed than ever and sat around, unable to work, unable to eat, unable to do anything but drown in self-pity and self-hate and bore the hell out of my friends on the telephone. I sat and waited for Bonnie to come home as I am told elderly who have been widowed sit and wait for their mates, who they feel have deserted them, to come back from the grave and take care of them.

In my pre-Bonnie days I had been entirely independent and self-sufficient, and if I had not exactly been a gourmet cook I was at least able to whip up a fairly convincing meat loaf. Now I found it so difficult to master the intricacies of heating up a kettle of water and making myself a cup of tea that I ate very little, and most of that in neighborhood diners.

Whenever the phone rang I was sure it was she. I would always let it ring three or four times before picking it up, then answer it in my most casual, debonair voice, and it would always be someone like the cleaning woman saying she couldn't come till Thursday.

One sunny Saturday I awoke in an uncharacteristically buoyant mood and decided that all I had to do to get Bonnie back was to be forceful and dynamic and not take any crap. After all, that was how I had gotten her to move in with me in the first place, wasn't it? Well then, that was how I was going to get her back. I dialed her number and my heart was whamming away so loudly in my ears that I could barely hear her when she answered.

"Hey," I said, "have you looked outside?"

"Uh, no," she said. "Why?"

"Well, it's just the most incredible day of the year, that's all. And I figured it would be a total waste if we didn't go for a walk in Central Park. How soon can you be ready?"

"Uh, well, I'm not sure I can go, exactly."

"Of *course* you can go," I said. "Now then, what time shall I pick you up?"

"Well . . ."

"Half an hour? Can you be ready in half an hour?"

"Half an hour? Well, I guess so, but—"

"Good. See you in half an hour."

"But I'm not really sure I—"

"Listen. I'm going to the park for a walk. I'd like to take you with me. But if I don't take *you* I'm going to take someone *else*. Now then, will you be ready in half an hour or won't you?"

"What's made you so damned peppy?" she said.

"Will you be ready in half an hour or won't you?"

"I . . . guess so," she said.

"Excellent. See you then."

I hung up the phone and jumped around the room with glee, ran into the bathroom to shower and shave, singing and laughing and generally carrying on like a lunatic. I finally had it—the forceful approach—and it was working. And even though it was completely an act it was going to do the trick. Bonnie's ambivalence and indecisiveness made her so malleable that anyone who took a really strong position with her could get her to do practically anything.

Just as I finished shaving the phone rang.

"Hello!" I sang out.

"Hi, it's Bonnie."

"Bonnie! I'm leaving the house in five minutes, sweetheart."

"Uh, yeah, listen. I don't think I'm going to be able to make it after all."

All of my false bravado leaked out of me like sand through a fist. "I see," I said.

"Yes. Well, the thing is that I had sort of promised my roommates I would help them give the apartment a thorough cleaning before I left for Connecticut with Louis, and, well, it really wouldn't be fair of me to disappoint them."

"No," I said, "it certainly wouldn't."

"But thanks for asking me anyway," she said. "It was a nice idea."

"Yes," I said, "it was."

I then entered a period of about a month of unbroken moping and inactivity. During this period Bonnie called two times, came over to get two more carloads of stuff, and I seem to remember we even had a little quibble about who *really* owned the teakettle and the floor squeegee. This was resolved, as I recall, by my keeping the teakettle and giving her the floor squeegee. I spent a great deal of time analyzing every dumb thing I had ever done in our relationship. I decided that Bonnie had finally come to hate me because she had hurt me, transferring her own guilt to my vulnerability. I kept thinking I saw her on the street, but it was never quite Bonnie, just girls with the same color hair and the same self-conscious slouching walk or the same brand of trench coat or something like that.

I learned from Mort—wonderful old Mort at the ad agency, who turned out to have been a great friend of Louis's and the one who'd urged Louis not to be shy about asking Bonnie out in the first place—that Bonnie was getting along better than ever at the agency, and that she and Louis were engaged to be married. Even though it had already been a few months since we'd broken up, I almost gagged on my tongue at the news.

Then a little while after that I heard that Bonnie had left old Louis for another man in the office, that Louis was completely shattered and despondent, and although I had never met the Hairless Wonder in my life, this news afforded me the first good laugh I'd had in half a year.

21

Eventually I recuperated sufficiently to appear in public at actual social gatherings. I had not yet truly recovered enough to do any real dating—how strange that prospect seemed to me and how sophomoric after the serious business of synthetic marriage and synthetic divorce I'd been through. But the ego wounds had scabbed over if not healed, and I was at least able to talk to strange girls without racing off to the bathroom.

I went to a party in the West Village one night and, since I'd come early and not many people had arrived yet, the girl friend of the host was obliged to talk to me. She was good-looking in a hard kind of way, and she was fairly amusing about herself. I hadn't been introduced to her, nor had we told each other our names, but I remember asking her what glib terrific people were expected, and with this perfectly straight face she said: "I understand that Dan Greenburg might be coming later."

I looked at her closely to see if she were putting me on, and I really couldn't tell. I asked her if she had ever met this guy Greenburg and who he was and what he was like, and she said that although she hadn't met him *personally* she had heard a lot about him, he was a writer, had written such-and-such a book and such-and-such an article, and that she'd heard he was fast and funny.

I burst out laughing at the concept of anyone thinking me fast or funny, and then I watched her figure it out. From the quality of embarrassment she displayed, I have to believe that she hadn't been putting me on.

The incident was sort of a turn-on for both of us, and I found my old powers of flirtation and seduction beginning to come back to me. I vaguely knew that the host was dating the girl, but I asked her to dinner for the following night anyway (ah there, Louis!), and she agreed to go.

We went to a fairly good, gimmicky restaurant with tricky menus and décor, and then I took her back to my apartment for drinks. Pretty soon we were necking on the bed and pretty soon we were petting outside-the-clothes-below-the-waist, and pretty soon it was inside-the-clothes-below-the-waist, and pretty soon I was stopped within millimeters of pay dirt.

I asked her what was wrong and she replied that she wasn't that kind of girl any more.

"Any more?" I said. *"What* anymore?"

"Well," she said, "up till about two weeks ago I generally went to bed with any guy who asked me. But that never worked out so hot, and so now it's all going to be different. It's going to be a whole other person now. A whole other-way-of-life kind of thing now."

"I see," I said. This sort of if-only-you-had-been-here-an-hour-ago routine had not been unknown to me in various forms during my dating days, and so I poked around in my old bag of tricks for some device to use on her.

When I finally came up with one I didn't trot it out for another half hour or so, and then I made it seem apropos of something else we were talking about. What I did was throw out the notion that I, too, seldom slept with people until I knew them really well—the reason, I explained almost blushingly, was that I found myself too vulnerable otherwise. What did I mean? she said. Well, I said, I tended to become quite emotionally involved with a woman after I'd been to bed with her and, since I'd recently been terribly hurt by a girl I'd been living with and engaged to marry, I didn't really think I could handle another deep emotional involvement for a while yet.

This obviously impressed her—the touching vulnerability (which was not wholly untrue), the having-recently-been-terribly-hurt thing, the concept that I had been Living With a Woman, the idea that I had already been Almost Married—and she quickly changed the subject.

About an hour later I again made a pass at her, and I was only somewhat surprised to find no resistance awaiting me at all. After it was over, I

281

asked her what had changed her mind.

She shrugged. "Just something you said," she said.

It was an important turning point for me. I had finally snapped out of my depression and self-disgust over Bonnie. I took out all my old dating lists and I added the initials of the hard-looking girl under those of Bonnie (below whom I had drawn a big double line in anticipation of the end of that phase of my life). And so, like it or not, I was back in the dating game again, and once more scoring.

A few more months and a few more sets of initials and then one night I finally met the lady who was to become my wife.

I guess I sort of knew she was going to become my wife, if not at the very moment I met her, then at least by the end of our first evening together. I don't mean it was your basic You-May-See-a-Stranger-Across-a-Crowded-Room kind of thing, because it was a little quieter than that. It's just that somewhere toward the end of our first date I remember thinking to myself: Oh yes, well, this lady here appears to be my wife. Hmmmm.

Needless to say, I didn't tell *her* that. Not for a while, at least. We started seeing each other several times a week right from the start, but I wanted to hold the whole thing at arm's length for a bit, then kind of ease on into it. I was still a little spooked on the idea of marriage and I didn't want to rush into anything I couldn't handle.

We saw each other every Monday, Wednesday

and Friday at first. Then every Monday, Wednesday, Friday and Sunday. Then every night but Tuesday and Thursday. Then every night but Thursday. The theory was that by holding out at least one night a week I still had my freedom. Freedom to guiltlessly jump whatever wanton female might amble into my lair of a Thursday evening, I suppose. Not many showed up, though, and I wasn't actively seeking them out, and soon I was calling up my as-yet-unknowing wife-to-be and saying things like: "I seem to find myself without a date tonight and, although I don't mean to establish any precedents, I figured that if you *also* didn't have a date tonight we might take in a movie or something."

Pretty soon I let her have her own special drawer in my chest of drawers, and pretty soon I let her bring over her hair dryer and her spice rack, and before I knew it she had gone and sublet her apartment and we were living together and there it was.

My ghastly thirtieth birthday had finally descended upon me. I would never again, even in my most egomaniacal moments, be able to think of myself as a boy wonder. Boy wonders become at the age of thirty merely moderately successful or even *very* successful men, but they are no longer boy *anythings*. Like the *New Yorker* cartoon of the kid with the violin on the stage of the Philharmonic pointing out that he was, after all, only six years old. Nobody's going to say: "Hey, that's pretty good for a kid of thirty." At thirty you finally become whatever it was you were becoming.

The great promise they saw in you has either been kept or broken. You are at thirty, willy-nilly, as close as you are ever likely to get to being a genuine grownup person.

I walked through Times Square one day and looked up at the accursed Accutron sign, on which you can watch not only the hours and minutes and seconds but also the *tenths* of seconds dribble off the end of your life on the huge bulb-studded digital clock, and I figured All Right. I figured Why Not. I figured, You've already gotten your first lousy marriage out of the way and possibly even learned a couple of things not to do the next time. I figured, So one of the reasons you're scared of marriage is that it brings you one life process closer to death, so remaining a bachelor isn't going to keep you from aging or from dying either. I figured, So you're scared of the total commitment of marriage, so what, so *everybody's* scared of that, so big goddam deal. I figured, you're thirty goddam years of age, which is nearly half your life, so what are you waiting for—let's get on with it already. Let's take the next step in life. Let's do it.

And as long as we're going to do it, I figured, let's do it right. Let's not make a chic little joke out of it. Let's not impulsively take a subway down to City Hall and get married in our levis by a guy with civil service things on his mind, looking like we've got better things to do. Let's play the whole thing out the way we're supposed to, the way we've been so carefully taught to. Let's go and have a fantastic dinner at the restaurant on top of the

Time-Life Building with the whole damned city spread out below us for our contemplation and let's propose in the formal, romantic, sentimental, time-honored, corny tradition we've learned about in songs and movies, and let's have a real honest-to-God wedding too, with a rabbi and everything else.

And then, mainly, Let's Get On With It.

The hottest heist since
The Anderson Tapes ...
by the author of
Miami Golden Boy.

MILLIONAIRES

by HERBERT KASTLE

The place was Bay Island, connected to Florida
by a narrow bridge. On it were twelve luxurious
homes, each one occupied by a millionaire. Even
the President of the United States, a frequent
visitor, was just another guest in the company
of the super-rich.

Walter Danforth "Bucky" Prince came to the
island with a distinguished family name, a repu-
tation as a super-stud and a handpicked crew of
helpers. His purpose was simple: to take over
Bay Island and loot it....

"Steaming sex, violence and suspense!"

Library Journal

A DELL BOOK $1.50

If you cannot obtain copies of this title from your local bookseller, just
send the price (plus 15c per copy for handling and postage) to Dell Books,
Post Office Box 1000, Pinebrook, N. J. 07058.

The big new scorcher by the sensational bestselling author of FIRE ISLAND ...

ACAPULCO

by Burt Hirschfeld

Acapulco—where the super-rich of the world gather . . . where a ruthless movie producer, a self-destructive sex queen and a brilliant, tormented writer are locked in a savage triangle of greed, lust and betrayal . . . Where millionaires and mystics, abandoned hedonists and dedicated artists seek their salvation and find their ultimate corruption—in the biggest, boldest, most blistering novel of the year!

"Smooth, sophisticated, erotic!"

—*New York Times*

A Dell Book $1.50

How many of these Dell Bestsellers have you read?

1. **IN THE SHADOW OF MAN**
   by Jane Van Lawick-Goodall $1.50

2. **THE GIFT HORSE**
   by Hildegard Knef $1.50

3. **THE WASHINGTON PAY-OFF**
   by Robert N. Winter-Berger $1.75

4. **BRIAN PICCOLO: A SHORT SEASON**
   by Jeannie Morris $1.25

5. **THE HAPPY HOOKER**
   by Xaviera Hollander $1.50

6. **THE MAGICIAN**
   by Sol Stein $1.25

7. **ACAPULCO**
   by Burt Hirschfeld $1.50

8. **THE NEW CENTURIONS**
   by Joseph Wambaugh $1.50

9. **DELIVERANCE**
   by James Dickey $1.25

10. **THE DISCIPLE AND HIS DEVIL**
    by Valerie Pascal $1.25

11. **THE MS. GIRLS**
    by Cheryl Nash $1.25

12. **MYSELF AMONG OTHERS**
    by Ruth Gordon $1.50

13. **THE JANE CASTLE MANUSCRIPT**
    by Philip L. Greene $1.25

If you cannot obtain copies of these titles from your local bookseller, just send the price (plus 15c per copy for handling and postage) to Dell Books, Post Office Box 1000, Pinebrook, N. J. 07058.